AN INTRODUCTION TO
6502 MACHINE CODE

by
R.A. & J.W. PENFOLD

GW00674627

BERNARD BABANI (publishing) LTD
THE GRAMPIANS
SHEPHERDS BUSH ROAD
LONDON W6 7NF
ENGLAND

PLEASE NOTE

Although every care has been taken with the production of this book to ensure that any projects, designs, modifications and/or programs etc. contained herein, operate in a correct and safe manner and also that any components specified are normally available in Great Britain, the Publishers do not accept responsibility in any way for the failure, including fault in design, of any project, design, modification or program to work correctly or to cause damage to any other equipment that it may be connected to or used in conjunction with, or in respect of any other damage or injury that may be so caused, nor do the Publishers accept responsibility in any way for the failure to obtain specified components.

Notice is also given that if equipment that is still under warranty is modified in any way or used or connected with home-built equipment then that warranty may be void.

All the programs in this book have been written and tested by the authors using models of the relevant micros that were available at the time of writing in Great Britain. Details of the graphics modes may vary with versions of these machines for other countries.

© 1984 BERNARD BABANI (publishing) LTD

First Published – August 1984
Reprinted – June 1986

British Library Cataloguing in Publication Data
Penfold, R.A.
  An introduction to 6502 machine code. –
(BP 147)
1. 6502 (Microprocessor) – Programming
2. Machine codes (Electronic computers)
I. Title   II. Penfold, J.W.
001.64'25   QA76.8.S63

ISBN 0 85934 122 4

Printed and bound in Great Britain by Cox & Wyman Ltd, Reading

CONTENTS

Page

PREFACE

Home computers are equipped with built-in software that enables them to be easily programmed to do quite complex tasks. The price that is paid for this programming ease is a relatively slow running speed, far lower than the speed at which the computer is really capable of running. Machine code programming entails direct programming of the microprocessor without using a built-in high level computer language such as BASIC. This gives a vast increase in running speed, but is something that can only really be undertaken by someone who has a reasonable understanding of the microprocessor and some of the other hardware in the computer.

Machine code programming is not as difficult as one might think, and once a few simple concepts have been grasped it is actually quite straightforward (although admittedly never as simple as using a high level language). This book takes the reader through the basics of microprocessors and machine code programming, and no previous knowledge of these are assumed.

The microprocessor dealt with here is the 6502, which is an excellent choice for beginners as it is in many ways a very simple type, but it is also very well designed and is acknowledged as one of the most powerful 8-bit microprocessors available. It is the microprocessor utilized in many of the popular home-computers, including the Electron, BBC Models A and B, VIC-20, ORIC-1/Atmos, and the Atari machines. The popular Commodore 64 uses the 6510 which is a slightly modified (but software compatible) version of the 6502. Some simple demonstration programs that can be run on a number of these machines are included in the book.

R. A. Penfold

Chapter 1

THE MICROPROCESSOR

All home computers are equipped to operate using a high level computer language such as BASIC or FORTH, and these languages are designed to make program design as quick and easy as possible. With most high level languages the programmer uses words that are virtually plain English, and the computer's built-in software then converts these into machine code routines that the processor at the heart of the computer can interpret and act upon. Writing programs direct in machine code is, on the face of it, rather pointless, as it is somewhat harder and a considerably slower process than using BASIC or another high level language to achieve the same ends.

The advantage of machine code programs is the speed with which they run. The speed of a machine code program is, in fact, only limited by the operating speed of the computer's microprocessor, and a computer can perform no faster than when it is running a machine code program. High level languages such as BASIC are inevitably much slower due to the way in which each instruction has to first be interpreted (converted into machine code) before it can be executed. In other words, the program is stored in memory in its BASIC form, and it is only when the program is run that each instruction is converted into machine code and executed. The program is effectively brought to a halt during the interpreting process, which accounts for more time than the running of the interpreted machine code. The difference in speed is probably much greater than most people realise, and machine code is typically something approaching one thousand times faster than an equivalent BASIC program. Action games written in BASIC are often a little sluggish due to this lack of operating speed, especially when a lot starts to happen at once, but a machine code equivalent normally appears to operate instantly no matter how much simultaneous action takes place. With some scientific and business programs BASIC is too slow to be of any use at all, and the use of machine code is mandatory. However, the speed of machine code is its only advantage, and apart (perhaps) from the fun of it, there is no point in using machine code where a program written in a high level language would be fast enough.

There are alternatives to machine code and high level interpreted languages such as BASIC, and we will consider these briefly before moving on to a description of the microprocessor itself. Some high level languages are compiled rather than interpreted. The difference is that with a compiled language the interpreting process is carried out before the program is run. The program may then run using the compiled machine code, or using a sort of pseudo machine code which requires a minimal amount of interpreting. In either case programs should run at high speed, and should be far easier to write than equivalent machine code programs. A compiled language may seem like the ideal solution (and many people would argue that it is), but languages of this type are generally much more difficult to use than interpreted languages when writing and debugging programs, and languages such as BASIC are probably much better for beginners to programming. A mixture of BASIC and machine code (with the latter only being used where high operating speed is essential) can therefore be a more practical solution in many cases.

Incidentally, you may come across the terms *source code* and *object code* occasionally. The former is the program in its high level language form, and the latter is the machine code or pseudo machine code produced after interpretation or compilation.

ASSEMBLY LANGUAGES

The terms machine code and assembly language seem to cause a certain amount of confusion, and there seems to be a general belief that they are different terms for the same thing. In fact they are very similar, but there is an important difference. With machine code programming the instructions for the

2

microprocessor are in the form of numbers from 0 to 255. This is not a very convenient way of doing things, and it inevitably involves almost constantly looking up instructions to find their code numbers. Assembly language uses a program in the computer to take three letter codes and convert these into the corresponding machine code instruction numbers. Most assemblers also provide the programmer with some further assistance, but not much. The basic function of the assembler is simply to take the three letter mnemonics and convert them to the appropriate numbers. An assembler is really the most basic of compilers, but as far as the programmer is concerned there is no real difference between assembly language and machine code, and if you can program in one you can also program using the other.

Of course, the main advantage of using an assembler is that the three letter mnemonics are chosen to closely relate to the instructions that they represent. For example, the Return From Subroutine instruction has RTS as its mnemonic, which is obviously much easier to remember than the machine code number of 60. If you intend to do a lot of machine code programming an assembler could reasonably be considered essential, since using anything other than a few short machine code routines is generally rather awkward and inconvenient with most home computers which are designed primarily for BASIC programming. A few computers (the Electron and BBC machines for instance) have built-in assemblers, but assembler programs are readily available for most other 6502 based computers. The facilities offered vary somewhat from one assembler to another, but most give at least some aid with debugging, although nothing like as much assistance as the best BASIC languages.

One final point to bear in mind is that a high level language like BASIC varies only slightly from one computer to another, and once you have mastered BASIC it is usually not too difficult to write programs for any computer equipped with this language. Problems can arise with the sound and graphics facilities which vary from one machine to another, giving inevitable variations in the sound and graphics commands. However, the language is fundamentally the same for all the computers that use it. Machine code programming is identical for any computers that use the 6502, and although there are again differences in the sound and graphics facilities available on various machines, these do not affect the instructions that are available to the programmer (although to produce the desired effect it might sometimes be necessary to use a different routine for each machine). The situation is very different when dealing with a computer that uses a different microprocessor such as the Z80A. Apart from the differences in the sound and graphics facilities, the microprocessor will have different machine code numbers for each instruction, and possibly even different mnemonics. Furthermore, the instruction sets of various microprocessors are substantially different, as are the registers they contain and the way in which they handle certain tasks. Obviously all microprocessors work on the same basic principle, but changing from programming one type to programming an alternative device usually involves a fairly substantial amount of work.

THE PROCESSOR

Although a microprocessor is an extremely complex device, usually containing the equivalent of tens of thousands of components, as far as the programmer is concerned it can be regarded as a fairly simple set of electrical circuits known as registers which will perform certain functions if fed with the appropriate instruction numbers. The registers consist of one or more circuits known as flip/flops, and these can produce an output voltage that is either virtually zero, or one that is typically about 5 volts. From the software point of view the voltages are not important, and we can think in terms of low or logic 0 if the output of a flip/flop is near zero volts, and high or logic 1 if it is at about 5 volts. A circuit with an output that can represent just 0 or 1 may not seem to be very useful, and in isolation such a circuit is not of tremendous value, but as we shall see later, a number of flip/flops together can represent large numbers, and can be used to perform complex calculations etc.

The registers of the 6502 are shown in diagramatic form in Figure 1, and the ones of main interest are the accumulator, the X register, and the Y register. These are all 8 bit registers. In other words, they have eight flip/flops and can handle numbers up to 8 bits long. A group of 8 bits is usually called a byte incidentally, although strictly speaking a byte does not have to be 8 bits long, and can be any length. The point about a byte is that it is not just a collection of unrelated signals or bits, but the bits operate together to represent a number, alphanumeric character, or whatever.

The accumulator is very much at the centre of things, and any data processed by the microprocessor has to be handled by this register and the complex circuit associated with it. This circuit is called the arithmetic logic unit, or ALU. If you feed an instruction to the microprocessor the ALU will almost certainly be involved in the execution of that instruction, but this is something that is all handled internally by the microprocessor itself, and the programmer does not get directly involved with the ALU. At this stage we will not consider in detail the type of data processing that the accumulator can provide, but it includes such things as addition and subtraction.

The X and Y registers are index registers. Their purpose is to act as pointers to tell the microprocessor where to find data or instructions. In order to understand their function it is necessary to understand, amongst other things, the basic make-up of a computer. Figure 2 shows in block diagram form the general arrangement used in a 6502 based computer. The memory is a bank of 8 bit registers which are used to store both program instructions and data. The number of registers in the memory block varies from one computer to another, but the 6502 can operate with a maximum of 65536. The address bus is 16 bits wide, and these sixteen bits are produced by the program counter (see Figure 1). It is the program counter, via the address bus, that selects the particular memory register that is connected to the microprocessor. The

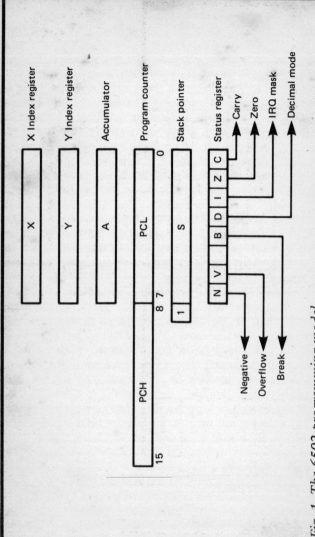

Fig. 1. The 6502 programming model

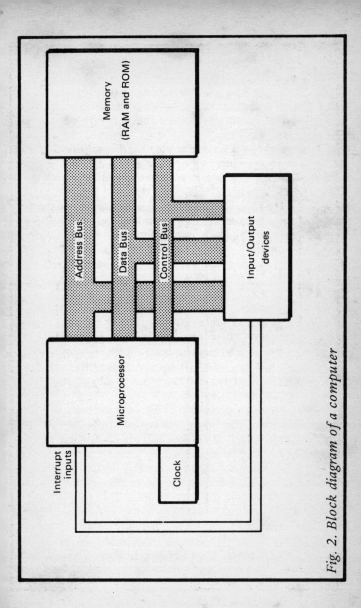

Fig. 2. Block diagram of a computer

7

data bus is used to transfer data between the microprocessor and the memory block. An important point to note here is that the data bus is bidirectional, and is used by the microprocessor to take data and instructions from memory, and to place data in memory. There are not separate input and output busses on a microprocessor, the data bus is used for both types of operation.

The control bus is used to make sure that all the elements of the system are operating in unison, and that if (say) the microprocessor sends data to a particular register in memory, that register is ready to receive that data and is not trying to output data to the microprocessor. All the lines in the control bus operate automatically, they are not directly controlled by the programmer, and are not something we need concern ourselves with here.

BINARY

The 16 bit program counter can place 65536 different output combinations onto the address bus, and it is this that limits the 6502 to 65536 memory registers. Each memory register occupies an address, which is merely a number from 0 to 65535, and each of the 65536 output combinations of the program counter corresponds to one of these addresses. Therefore, by placing each bit of the program counter at the appropriate state, the microprocessor can read the contents of any memory register, or can write data to that register depending on the type of instruction it is executing. In order to undertake machine code or assembly language programming it is essential to understand the way in which the bits of the address bus (and the data bus) are used to represent a number.

The numbering system we normally use, in every day life, is commonly called the decimal system and is, of course, based on the number 10. There are ten single digit numbers from 0 to 9. This system of numbering is not very convenient for an electronic circuit in that it is difficult to devise a practical system where an output has ten different voltage levels so that any single digit decimal number can be represented. It is much easier to use simple flip/flops which have just two output levels, and can only represent 0 or 1. However, this bars such circuits from operating directly in the decimal numbering system, and instead, the binary system of numbering is utilized.

This system is based on the number 2 rather than 10, and the highest single digit number is 1 rather than 9. If we take a decimal number such as 238, the 8 represents eight units (10 to the power of 0), the 3 represents three tens (10 to the power of 1), and the 2 represents two hundreds (10 to the power of 2, or 10 squared). Things are similar with a binary number such as 1101. Working from right to left again, the 1 represents the number of units (2 to the power of 0), the 0 represents the number of twos (2 to the power of 1), the next 1 represents the number of fours (2 to the power of 2), and the final 1 represents the number of eights (2 to the power of 3). 1101 in binary is therefore equivalent to 13 in decimal ($1 + 0 + 4 + 8 = 13$).

The table following shows the number represented by each digit of a 16 bit number when it is set high. Of course, a bit always represents zero when it is set low.

Bit	0	1	2	3	4	5	6	7	8
	1	2	4	8	16	32	64	128	256

Bit	9	10	11	12	13	14	15
	512	1024	2048	4096	8192	16384	32768

Using 16 bits any integer from 0 to 65535 can be represented in binary fashion, or using 8 bits any integer from 0 to 255 can be represented, and this exposes the main weakness of the binary numbering system. Numbers of modest magnitude are many binary digits in length, but despite this drawback the ease with which electronic circuits can handle binary numbers makes this system the only practical one at the present time.

9

Addition of two binary numbers is a straightforward business which is really more simple than decimal addition. A simple example is shown below:—

First number	11110000
Second number	01010101
Answer	101000101

As with decimal addition, start with the units column and gradually work towards the final column on the left. In this case there is 1 and 0 in the units column, giving a total of 1 in the units column of the answer. In the next column two 0s give 0 in the answer, and the next two columns are equally straightforward. In the fifth one there are two 1s to be added, giving a total of 2. Of course, in binary the figure 2 does not exist, and this should really be thought of as 10 (one 2 and no units), and it is treated in the same way as ten in decimal addition. The 0 is placed in the answer and the 1 is carried forward to the next column of figures. The sixth column again gives a total of 10, and again the 0 is placed in the answer and the 1 is carried forward. In the seventh column this gives a total of 3 in the decimal, but in this binary calculation it must be thought of as the binary number 11 (one 2 and one unit). Therefore, 1 is placed in the answer and 1 is carried forward. In the eighth column this gives an answer of 10, and as there are no further columns to be added, both digits are placed in the answer.

Adding two 8 bit binary numbers together produces a slight complication in that, as in this case, the answer is some 9 bits long. When the accumulator is used to add two 8 bit numbers it cannot accommodate the extra bit when there is a final carry-forward, but the 1 in column nine is not simply lost (which would obviously give an incorrect answer and would be unacceptable). Instead, the carry-forward is taken to one of the status registers of the microprocessor. Not surprisingly, this is called the carry or C register. Like the other status registers this is used to control conditional instructions (i.e. if the carry bit is set high do this, if it is not do that). Anyone who has done some BASIC programming should be familiar with conditional instructions in the form of BASIC IF . . . THEN or IF . . . THEN . . . ELSE instructions.

Of course, the fact that the accumulator can only handle 8 bit numbers giving a maximum equivalent to 255 in decimal, is not to say that computers and microprocessors cannot deal in numbers of a higher magnitude. Very large numbers can be accommodated by using two or more bytes together. The usual way of doing this is to have (say) two bytes used together with one byte providing the lower 8 bits of the number, and the other providing the upper 8 bits. These are generally called the low byte and high byte respectively. Two other terms that are often used are least significant bit or LSB, and most significant bit or MSB. These simply refer to the lowest and highest bits respectively (e.g. bits 0 and 7 of a 8 bit number).

When adding together two 16 bit numbers the basic way in which it is done is to first add the two low bytes, to give the low byte of the answer. Then the two high bytes are added together with the carry (if any) to give the high byte of the answer, plus a possible 17th bit in the carry flag.

When machine code programming using a home computer the hardware between the programmer and the microprocessor can help to make things very much easier, but it can also be a hinderance. Few home computers (in fact no 6502 based machines as far as I am aware) allow numbers to be entered in binary form, or normally display data in this form. Thus, although the microprocessor would handle a calculation such as 10 plus 20 in binary form, using a home computer the numbers would be entered in decimal, and the answer would be displayed in decimal. For simple data processing this is very convenient, but when it comes to multi-byte numbers and certain other types of data processing it is rather inconvenient. A large number such as 2050 is processed by the microprocessor as two 8 bit numbers, which are entered into the computer as two decimal numbers in the range 0 to 255. In the case of the number 2050, in decimal

11

the high byte is 4, and the low byte is 2, which bears little resemblence to the decimal number 2050 or its binary equivalent. The point to remember here is that bits 0 to 7 of the high byte represent the 512s, 1024s, 2048s, etc., through to the 32768s. However, as far as the number entered into the computer is concerned, when set high bits 0 to 7 only represent 1, 2, 4, etc.

When using machine code you must be aware of the way in which the microprocessor deals with data on a bit by bit basis if you are to fully master the situation, and a reasonable understanding of binary is essential.

SIGNED BINARY

The binary system described so far, which is often called direct binary, is inadequate in many practical applications in that it is unable to handle negative numbers. One way around the problem is to use signed binary numbers where the first bit is used to denote whether the number is positive or negative. The convention has the first bit as a 0 for positive numbers and as a 1 for negative numbers. With this system the normal number range of 0 to 255 is replaced with a range of −127 (11111111) to +127 (01111111). The problem is solved only at the expense of reduced maximum magnitude for a given number of bits. Note though, that where two or more bytes are used to form a multi-byte number, only the most significant bit of the high byte needs to be used to indicate whether the number is positive or negative, and it is not necessary to use the most significant bit of each byte in the number to do this.

Obviously a certain amount of care needs to be exercised when dealing with binary numbers and you must know whether a number is in signed or unsigned binary. For example, 10000001 could be 129 (unsigned) or −1 (signed). In this basic form the signed binary system has practical limitations in that it can represent binary numbers without any difficulty, but calculations fail to give the right result, which makes the system of little practical value unless it is modified to correct this anomaly. It is not used with the 6502 microprocessor in the basic form described above.

To illustrate the problem, consider the calculation shown below:—

16	00010000
−5	10000101
Answer (−21)	10010101

Adding 16 to −5 should obviously give an answer of 11 and not −21.

An alternative and related method of handling negative numbers is the ones complement system. Here a negative number is the complementary of the positive equivalent. For instance, +16 in binary is 00010000, and −16 is therefore 11101111. In other words, the ones are simply changed to zeros and the zeros are changed to ones. This gives better results when used in calculations, as demonstrated by the example given below:—

16	00010000
−5	11111010
Answer (266)	100001010

This answer may seem to be less use than the one obtained using ordinary signed binary, and the margin of error is certainly greater, but this depends on how the answer is interpreted. The first point to note is that the positive number starts with a zero and the negative number starts with a 1. Provided that sufficient digits are used this will always be the case, and in this respect the system is not much different to ordinary signed binary. The answer is completely wrong of course, but if the carry is ignored the answer is much closer to the right result. It then becomes 10 rather than 11. So what happens if we try another example and again ignore the carry in the answer?

32	0010000
-4	1111011
Answer (27)	00011011

As before, the answer is wrong, but is one less than the right answer (which is of course 28 in this case).

TWOS COMPLEMENT

Clearly this system can be made to operate properly, and it is just a matter of finding some way of correcting the answer. The method used with simple microprocessors such as the 6502 is the twos complement system. This differs from the ones complement system in that once the compliment of a number has been produced one is added to it. Therefore, rather than -5 being represented as 11111010, it becomes 11111011. If we now apply this to one of the examples given earlier we obtain the following result:—

16	00010000
-5	11111011
Answer (11)	00001011

This time, provided we ignore the carry in the carry flag, we have the correct answer of 11. This is a convenient way of handling subtraction (for the microprocessor anyway) since subtraction can be handled by the same circuit that handles addition. To handle a sum such as $45 - 25$ the figure of 25 is converted into (twos complement) -25, and then added to 45. In other words, rather than calculating the sum in the form $45 - 25$ the microprocessor calculates it as $45 + (-25)$, and either way the answer is 20.

The table given below shows some sample numbers in twos complement form, and should help to clarify the system for you. Note that, like ordinary signed binary, the first digit is used to indicate whether the number is positive or negative.

Numbers	Positive	Negative
0	00000000	00000000
1	00000001	11111111
2	00000010	11111110
3	00000011	11111101
4	00000100	11111100
32	00100000	11100000
126	01111110	10000010
127	01111111	10000001
128	010000000	10000000

Note that with 8 bit twos complement numbers the range is from +127 to −128.

So far we have only considered calculations where the answer is a positive quantity, but the twos complement system works properly if the answer is negative. The following example demonstrates this point:—

16	00010000
−31	11100001
Answer (−15)	11110001

The system also functions correctly when two negative numbers are added together, as demonstrated by this example:—

−4	11111100
−8	11111000
Answer (−12)	11110100

OVERFLOW FLAG

When using the twos complement system there is a slight problem in that a number can be accidentally turned into a negative quantity. The simple calculation shown below demonstrates this point:—

64	01000000
127	01111111
Answer (−65)	10111111

If taken as an ordinary 8 bit direct binary number this does give the right answer, but in the twos complement system the carry forward from bit 6 to bit 7 has changed the sign and magnitude of the number so that an answer of −65 instead of 191 is obtained.

This is termed an overflow, and it is handled by microprocessors such as the 6502 by a flag called (appropriately) the overflow flag. In the diagram of Figure 1 this is given its abbreviated name, the V flag. Like the carry flag, there are special instructions connected with this flag, and these can be used to prevent erroneous results from being produced, or to give warning that an error has occurred. These flags are normally at 0 and are set by an overflow or a carry forward. They are automatically reset by some of the microprocessor's instructions, and this helps to streamline things so that the system operates rapidly and uses as little memory as possible. There are also instructions to specifically reset one flag or the other.

At this stage it is probably best not to go into any more detail about binary calculations and the way they are handled by microprocessors. It is a complicated subject, and it is probably clarified most easily by trying out a few programs which demonstrate the techniques involved. Some practical examples that can be run on some popular 6502 based home computers are given later in this book. Even if you can only understand direct binary, provided you also understand the main principles of microprocessors you should be able to run and understand some simple machine code routines.

BINARY CODED DECIMAL

The 6502 can use another form of binary known as binary coded decimal, or BCD. This is perhaps less frequently used than the twos complement binary system described above, and it has the disadvantages of being relatively slow and uneconomic on memory. However, it can be used to give a high degree of precision, and it can be advantageous in certain applications. It is certainly worthwhile considering this system briefly here.

With BCD four binary bits (often termed a nibble) are used to represent each decimal digit. The system operates in the manner shown below:—

Decimal Number	Bit Code
0	0000
1	0001
2	0010
3	0011
4	0100
5	0101
6	0110

17

7	0111
8	1000
9	1001

The binary number is in fact just the normal binary representation of the number concerned, and it is only for numbers of more than 9 that the system is different. The binary codes from 1010 to 1111 are unused, and all two digit decimal numbers require 8 bit binary codes. For instance, the decimal number 64 would be represented by the 8 bit BCD code 01100100. The first four bits (0110) represent the 6, and the second four bits (0100) represent the 4. Each byte can therefore represent any two bit number from 0 to 99, which compares to a range of 0 to 255 for a straightforward 8 bit binary number. This helps to contribute to the relative inefficiency of the BCD system. Of course, when a nibble is incremented by 1 from 1001 (9 in decimal) it does not go to 1010 (which is an illegal code in BCD), but cycles back to 0000. A carry forward of 1 should then be taken to the next BCD nibble.

With this system there is no difficulty in handling large numbers, and it is just a matter of using several bytes to accommodate the required number of digits. Negative numbers and decimal points can also be handled with ease by this system, but this requires an additional byte or bytes. This information is usually carried in the high byte or bytes.

HEXADECIMAL

While on the subject of numbering systems it would perhaps be worthwhile dealing with another system which you will inevitably come across quite frequently, and this is the hexa-decimal system. There is in fact yet another system known as octal which, as its name suggests, is based on the number 8. Octal seems to have fallen from favour in recent years, and as it is something you are not likely to encounter these days we will not consider this system here.

A problem with binary numbers is that they tend to have many digits with each digit being either 0 or 1, which makes them rather difficult to deal with in many circumstances. For instance, trying to remember more than just a very few 6502 instruction codes in their 8 bit binary form would probably be beyond most people's ability. On the other hand, binary numbers give a graphic representation of the state of each bit in the registers of the microprocessor, and this is something that is often important. Decimal numbers are easier to use in that they are much shorter and are in a familiar form. Converting a decimal number into an equivalent binary one is not a very quick and easy process, especially where large numbers are concerned, and this is inconvenient when it is necessary to visualise things on a bit by bit basis.

The hexadecimal system gives the best of both worlds in that it requires just a few digits to represent fairly large numbers, and is in fact slightly better than the decimal system in this respect. On the other hand, it is easy to convert hexadecimal to binary, and it is easy to use when operating at bit level. The hexadecimal system is based on the number 16, and there are sixteen single digit numbers. Obviously the numbers we normally use in the decimal system are inadequate for hexadecimal as there are six too few of them, but this problem is overcome by augmenting them with the first six letters of the alphabet. It is from this that the system derives its name. The table following helps to explain the way in which the hexadecimal system operates.

What makes hexadecimal so convenient is the way in which multidigit numbers can be so easily converted into binary form. The reason for this is that each hexadecimal digit represents four binary bits. Take the hexadecimal A3 in the above table for instance. The digit A represents 1010 in binary, and the digit three converts to 0011. A3 therefore represents 10100011 in binary. You may find that you can memorise the four bit binary number represented by each of the sixteen hexadecimal digits, but a little mental arithmetic

Decimal	Hexadecimal	Binary
0	0	0000
1	1	0001
2	2	0010
3	3	0011
4	4	0100
5	5	0101
6	6	0110
7	7	0111
8	8	1000
9	9	1001
10	A	1010
11	B	1011
12	C	1100
13	D	1101
14	E	1110
15	F	1111
16	10	00010000
17	11	00010001
163	A3	10100011

is all that is needed to make the conversion if you cannot.
The digits in a hexadecimal number represent, working from right to left, the number of units 16s, 256s, 4096s, 65536s, and 1048576s. You are unlikely to use hexadecimal numbers of more than six digits in length.

SYSTEM OPERATION

If we now return to the block diagrams of Figures 1 and 2, you should begin to get the idea of how data is moved around the system and processed. At switch on the microprocessor has all the registers set to zero, apart from the program counter which starts at a certain address. The start up procedure is not normally of interest to the machine code programmer, since few people design their own systems. It is far more likely that you will be using a home computer where all this is taken care of by the computer's operating system. The program you write will normally go into a section of memory occupied by random access memory (RAM). This is memory where the microprocessor can set its contents at any desired 8 bit binary number, and then read back that number at a later time. The contents of RAM can be changed an unlimited number of times, but reading the contents of RAM does not destroy the data there or affect it in any way. However, when the computer is switched off the contents of RAM are lost. Software such as the computer's operating system and BASIC interpreter are usually in read only memory (ROM) which retains its contents after the computer has been switched off (although the BASIC interpreter or other language has to be loaded from tape or disc on a few machines). The contents of ROM are fixed, and writing to ROM does not alter its contents. ROM is not an area of memory that is normally used by the programmer, the exception being when there are useful routines there that can be utilized.

The block marked input/output in Figure 2 includes such things as the keyboard and the chip which produces the television picture. The 6502 uses memory mapped input/output. In other words, the microprocessor reads data from or writes data to input/output devices just as if they were RAM, and they are addressed in exactly the same way. This has the advantage of making programming more straightforward in that using a common set of instructions for memory and input/output operations gives fewer instructions to contend with. A minor drawback is that some of the 64k (a k is 1024 bytes incidentally) memory address range is occupied by the input/output devices, but this does not normally seriously deplete the maximum amount of memory that can be included.

With the aid of the computer's operating system and either the BASIC interpreter or an assembler, the machine code program is placed in a suitable section of memory, and the program is run by directing the microprocessor to the appropriate address. The machine code program then operates by fetching an instruction from the start address of the program, and then shuffling data around its registers and the memory as it goes through the set of instructions. This may seem a rather vague description of things, but if you can grasp the basic concept of instructions and data being taken from memory, or possibly input/output devices, with the data being processed in some way by the microprocessor before being sent back to a memory location or an output device, then you should not find it difficult to understand a few simple machine code programs and then gradually progress to more complex ones. If you cannot see how the system operates overall, individual machine code instructions could, to say the least, be rather difficult to understand, and even simple programs would certainly be impossible to follow.

A simple example of how the system operates should now be quite easy for you to understand. We will assume that the program must take a number from one memory location, then add this to a number taken from a second address, and then finally place the answer at a third address. There is more than one way of going about this, and the differences occur due to the various addressing modes that the 6502 can use. In other words, we can place the numbers at any addresses we like, and by using the appropriate addressing mode (or modes) and instructions the program can be made to obtain the numbers from the correct addresses. Addressing modes is a fairly complex subject which is fully discussed in a later chapter of this book, and it will not be considered in detail here. For the sake of this example we will use the most simple addressing mode, which is immediate addressing. With this system the first instruction would be to load a byte into the accumulator from memory (i.e. the first number), and with immediate addressing the byte of data is at the address which follows the instruction. After receiving an immediate instruction the program counter automatically increments by one and moves the program on to the byte of data that is to be processed. The next instruction would be to add the second number to the number currently in the accumulator, and this would again be a matter of having the instruction followed by the number at the next address. Next, the instruction to store the accumulator at the next address would be used, and then finally the return from subroutine instruction would be given. This last instruction simply ends the program and returns control of the computer to the operating system.

This program only uses seven bytes including the one where the answer is stored. Before the program was run these would be as follows:—

Byte 1	Load immediate instruction code
Byte 2	First number
Byte 3	Add immediate instruction code
Byte 4	Second number
Byte 5	Store accumulator immediate instruction
Byte 6	Any 8 bit number
Byte 7	Return from subroutine instruction

After the program was run things would be little different, and the only change would be that byte 6 would have been changed from a random number to the sum of the first and second numbers. In this simple example we are ignoring any carry forward indicated by the carry flag.

It is only fair to point out that the program could not be run in this form on the 6502 as it does not have the store accumulator instruction in its immediate form. However, it could achieve much the same thing using an alternative form of this instruction, and this gives us an opportunity to briefly

23

consider the use of the X and Y index registers. With the immediate instructions the program counter automatically increments by one after the microprocessor has finished the instruction. This method of doing things is very fast, straightforward, and requires little memory, but it is in many ways limiting.

The X and Y registers can be loaded with numbers which can then be used to control the program counter in some way so that the program jumps to the required address. In our simple example this indexed addressing is an unnecessarily complicated way of doing things, but it nevertheless illustrates the use of an index register, and should give you the basic idea of how they are used.

Using indexed addressing to store the answer the program would be along the lines shown below:—

Byte 1	Load accumulator immediate
Byte 2	First number
Byte 3	Add accumulator immediate
Byte 4	Second number
Byte 5	Load X register immediate
Byte 6	Offset to be loaded into X register
Byte 7	Store accumulator absolute X
Byte 8	8 least significant bits of address
Byte 9	8 most significant bits of address
Byte Z	Answer
Byte Z+1	Return from subroutine

The program starts in the same way as before, but at bytes 5 and 6 we are loading a number into the X register. When the store accumulator instruction is reached it is followed by a 16 bit address in the next two bytes. Note that the least significant bits are given first, followed by the most significant bits, and not as one might expect, with the most significant bits first. The answer is stored at address Z, which is the 16 bit address at bytes 8 and 9 plus the offset which was loaded earlier into the X register. This can be any address within the 64k address range of the 6502. The program then goes to the next byte (address Z+1, not Byte 10) where the return from subroutine instruction is used to hand control back to the computer's operating system.

Something that will probably have become apparent is that it takes a large number of machine code instructions to achieve quite simple tasks. When programming in a language such as BASIC each instruction is converted into a number of machine code instructions by the interpreter. This is one of the factors which makes writing machine code programs a relatively slow affair.

THE STACK

There are a number of registers in the 6502 (and shown in Figure 1) which we have not yet considered, and we will take a look at the function of these now. The one labelled S is the stack pointer, and this is actually a 9 bit register rather than the more usual (for the 6502 anyway) 8 bit type. However, the most significant bit is always set at 1. The stack is a set of registers which can be used for temporary data storage, and with some microprocessors the stack is an internal part of the microprocessor. This is often termed a hardware stack. This is in many ways the most elegant solution to the problem, and it has the advantage of high speed. It has the disadvantage of giving only a relatively small number of registers, and does of course add complexity to the microprocessor.

The 6502, in common with most of the more simple microprocessors, uses the alternative of a software stack. This is just an area of memory which is reserved for use as the stack, and the system must, of course, provide RAM at the relevant range of addresses. The stack pointer (the S register) points to an address in this block of RAM, and with the 6502 the

25

stack extends from 100000000 to 111111111 in binary, or 256 to 511 in decimal. The stack register operates automatically, and it is not like an index register which can be loaded with any desired 8 bit number. The stack uses the last in—first out or LIFO system. In other words, each time data is placed onto the stack the S register is incremented by 1, and each time data is taken from the stack the pointer is automatically decremented by one. This is often looked on as being analogous to a stack of plates, with plates being loaded one on top of the other, building a pile from the bottom upwards, and then removing plates from the top of the pile and working downwards. This analogy does not work too well with the 6502 as it starts with the stack pointer at 111111111 and counts downwards as the stack is enlarged. However, the last in—first out doctrine still applies. The fact that the stack grows downwards is really only of academic importance anyway, since the stack pointer increments and decrements automatically.

Apart from use as a convenient temporary data store, the stack is also used when subroutines and interrupts are implemented. We will not consider these in detail here, but in both cases the microprocessor breaks out of its normal operating routine, and branches off into another routine. With an interrupt, the signal to the microprocessor that it must break out of its normal routine is provided by a hardware device via one of the 6502's two interrupt inputs. A typical application where interrupts are used is the timer that is a feature of many home computers. Here a counter circuit generates an interrupt (say) every 10 milliseconds, and a software routine is used to increment by one the number stored at a set of memory locations. With suitable manipulation the number in these RAM locations can be converted into suitable data for a minutes and seconds display, or even for a real-time clock. The number can be POKEd to any desired figure so that the clock can be set at the required time. If the timer is to achieve a reasonable degree of accuracy it is important that the microprocessor carries out the software routine at each request without waiting to complete other tasks first. It is for this type of application that interrupts are ideal.

The problem with the use of interrupts is that the microprocessor has to be able to break back into its main routine again after it has finished the interrupt routine. To facilitate this things such as the contents of the accumulator, the X register, and the Y register are stored on the stack when the interrupt is generated, and then retrieved again when the interrupt routine has been completed. Things are much the same when a subroutine is called; and a subroutine could be regarded as a software generated interrupt. In fact there is a 6502 instruction (break) which has exactly the same effect as an interrupt request. When writing programs for home computers it is unlikely that you will need to deal with interrupts, and they are principally used as part of the computer's operating system and in a few specialised add-on hardware applications. Because the computer is continually generating its own interrupts there will almost certainly be restrictions on the use of user generated interrupts, and they may not be usable at all.

FLAGS

The 6502 has status flags apart from the carry and overflow ones, and one of these is the zero flag (the Z register of Figure 1). This is used by conditional instructions which test to see whether or not this bit is set. As its name suggests, this bit is set when the result of an operation by the arithmetic logic unit has produced zero as the answer.

The negative flag (the N register of Figure 1) is equally straightforward, and this bit is set when the result of an operation by the arithmetic logic unit gives a negative result.

The I flag is the interrupt masking bit, and this can be set by the programmer to disable certain interrupts. The D flag is the decimal flag, and this is set to place the 6502 in the BCD mode.

PAGING

When dealing with the 6502 it is common to find references to pages of memory. For example, you will often come across references to zero page. Pages of memory are simply blocks of 256 bytes, with zero page at address from 0 to 255, page 1 at 256 to 511, page 2 at 512 to 767, and so on. The 64k address range of the 6502 gives 256 pages in all. As we have already seen, page 1 is used as the stack, but the other pages are free for the system designer to use virtually in any way he or she desires.

Although the use of paging may seem pointless, it can be helpful. Due to the use of 8 bit index registers in the 6502 the page boundaries are real rather than imaginary when some addressing modes are used, and although there is no difficulty in crossing the boundaries in these modes, extra instructions (and processing time) are involved.

6502 PINOUTS

The 6502 is contained in a 40 pin DIL plastic package, and it has the pinout configuration shown in Figure 3. The pinouts of the device are really only of academic importance as far as the programmer is concerned, but a brief description of these will be given here as you might find it helpful in understanding how the overall system operates.

The pins marked A0 to A15 are the 16 bit address bus, and similarly, D0 to D7 are the 8 bit data bus. IRQ is the interrupt request input, and taking this low generates an interrupt, but the current instruction is completed first, and the microprocessor would simply crash if it was not. Then the interrupt mask bit of the status register is examined, and the interrupt sequence will only be started if the interrupt mask bit is not set. The processor automatically stores the contents of the program counter and the status register on the stack, and it also sets the interrupt mask bit so that further interrupts are ignored until the current one has been completed. This is

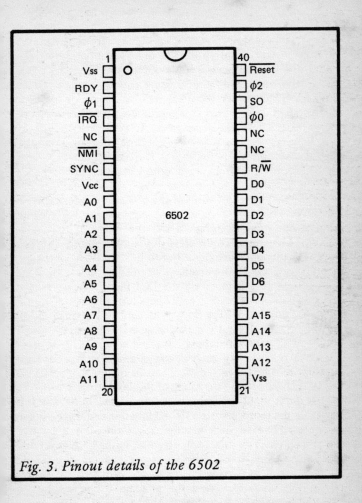

Fig. 3. Pinout details of the 6502

obviously essential, since the microprocessor is then loaded with the numbers stored at (hexadecimal) addresses FFFE (low byte) and FFFF (high byte). These two addresses must therefore contain the start address of the interrupt routine.

An important point to bear in mind regarding interrupts is that the microprocessor only saves (on the stack) and restores the contents of the program counter and the status register. If any other registers, such as the X or Y index registers, will have their contents altered by the interrupt routine, it is up to the programmer to provide a routine to save these on the stack and then restore them again at the end of the interrupt routine. The programmer is also responsible for resetting the interrupt masking bit once the interrupt has been serviced.

The second interrupt input of the 6502 is the non-maskable interrupt (NMI) input. As its name suggests, this has a higher priority than the IRQ input, and the interrupt routine is performed regardless of the state of the interrupt masking bit. Obviously this interrupt input has to be used with some care. In other respects the interrupt is handled in much the same way as for one generated via the IRQ input. However, the program counter is loaded with the address stored at (hexadecimal) addresses FFFA (low byte) and FFFB (high byte). Thus there is no difficulty in having separate interrupt routines for the IRQ and NMI inputs. It is actually possible to have several devices driving each interrupt input, with a separate interrupt routine for each device, but the methods of achieving this really goes beyond the scope of this book.

The Reset input is taken low briefly at switch on, and this starts the microprocessor on its initialisation sequence. It can also be used to take the computer back to this sequence at any time, such as after the computer has crashed. Many 6502 based computers have a Reset or Break switch which simply pulls the Reset pin low when the switch is operated. As part of the initialisation process the program counter is loaded with the numbers at (hexadecimal) addresses FFFC (low byte) and FFFD (high byte), and these direct the microprocessor to the start of the operating system routine.

The read/write (R/W) pin is an output, and is used to control memory and input/output devices. It goes high when the microprocessor is reading the data bus, and it switches the memory and input/output devices into the output mode so that the relevant device can be read by the microprocessor. Of course, only one device at a time must output data onto the data bus, and correct decoding of the address bus ensures that only one device is activated at any one time. The read/write line goes low when the microprocessor is placing data onto the data bus, and this sets the memory and input/output devices in the state where they are ready to receive data from the data bus. Again, correct decoding of the data bus ensures that only the intended device receives the data written onto the data bus by the microprocessor.

The pins marked $\phi0$, $\phi1$ and $\phi2$ are the clock terminals of the device, and the 6502 has a built-in clock circuit which has its frequency set by an external crystal. The clock simply provides a series of electrical pulses to the microprocessor, and it is these that move the component through the complex sequence of events that make up each instruction. The standard 6502 will operate with clock frequencies of up to 1 megahertz (i.e. one million pulses a second), and it is normally used with a clock frequency at something in the region of 1 MHz so that it carries out instructions at something approaching the highest rate possible. When using the 6502 (or any microprocessor) in an application where high operating speed is important it must be remembered that each instruction takes several clock cycles, and that a clock frequency of 1 megahertz does not equate with 1 million instructions per second. The number of cycles taken to execute an instruction varies from one instruction to another, but for the 6502 it is typically about six clock cycles.

There are higher speed versions of the 6502, such as the 6502C, but these differ from the standard 6502 only in the maximum clock frequency that can be used. As far as programming is concerned there is no difference between the various versions of the 6502.

MEMORY ORGANISATION

The manual for most home computers includes a memory map, which shows the functions of various parts of the computer's address range. The memory map varies considerably from one computer to another, but there are strong similarities between maps for the various 6502 based home computers. Figure 4 shows a typical 6502 home computer memory map. This is not the map for any particular computer incidentally, and is a sort of generalised 6502 memory map.

As pointed out earlier, page 1 is used as the stack, and this is something that will obviously be common to all 6502 based machines. Zero page is usually reserved for important variables and pointers, and this is due to the special form of addressing associated with zero page (which is discussed in more detail in the next chapter). Of course, there has to be RAM at pages 0 and 1 due to the variable nature of the data that will be stored there, and so the RAM starts at zero page and extends upwards. As we have seen, the six addresses at the top of memory point to the start addresses of the operating system and interrupt routines, and the operating system ROM therefore occupies the top section of the address range. It is convenient to have the language ROM immediately beneath this in the memory map. The top part of the RAM is normally used as the video display RAM, and this is convenient in that with most computers the amount of RAM required for the display depends on the display mode used. With this system it is easy to arrange things so that as less RAM is utilized by the display, more RAM automatically becomes available for program use, with the boundary between the two changing according to the display mode used. Of course, not all computers use the full 64k address range and can operate in this way, but these days the majority seem to do so, or have the option of extra RAM which brings them into this category.

The area of memory used for input/output devices tends to vary considerably from one machine to another. Perhaps the

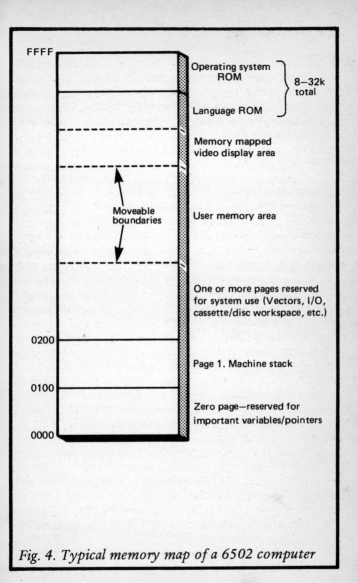

Fig. 4. Typical memory map of a 6502 computer

most logical place for it is low in memory, such as the page 3 input/output used by the ORIC-1 and Atmos computers. On the other hand, many home computers have some unused ROM space, and it then makes sense to fit the input/output devices into this area of memory so that as much space as possible is left free for RAM to hold programs. This is the input/output system used in computers such as the BBC machines and the Electron.

Chapter 2

THE 6502 INSTRUCTION SET

This chapter is an alphabetical list of all the legal 6502 instructions, giving a brief description of the operation performed, the opcodes for all the address modes available with a particular instruction, and a list of the flags affected. All opcodes are given in hexadecimal notation.

The number of bytes and number of cycles taken by each instruction are not given here. Information on instruction length is given in the next chapter (Address Modes), and number of cycles taken is given in the instruction set chart at the back of the book.

1. ADD WITH CARRY

Mnemonic — ADC

Adds the contents of the memory address or immediate data to the contents of the accumulator and carry bit. The result is placed in the accumulator. The CLC instruction may be used before ADC to add without carry. This instruction may be used in either binary or decimal mode.

The N, V, Z and C flags are affected by this instruction.

Address mode	Opcode
Absolute	6D
Zero-page	65
Immediate	69
Absolute, X	7D
Absolute, Y	79
(Indirect, X)	61

(Indirect, Y)	71
Zero-page, X	75

2. LOGIC AND

Mnemonic AND

Logical ANDs the specified data with the contents of the accumulator on a bit-by-bit basis. The result is placed in the accumulator.

Flags affected are N and Z.

Logical AND operates according to the following rules:—

1 AND 1 = 1

1 AND 0 = 0

0 AND 0 = 0

Address mode	Opcode
Absolute	2D
Zero-page	25
Immediate	29
Absolute, X	3D
Absolute, Y	39
(Indirect, X)	21
(Indirect, Y)	31
Zero-page, X	35

3. ARITHMETIC SHIFT LEFT

Mnemonic ASL

Shifts the contents of memory location or accumulator left by one bit position. Bit 0 is set to 0, bit 7 is placed in the carry bit. The result is placed in the source.

Flags affected are N, Z and C.

Address mode	Opcode
Accumulator	0A
Absolute	0E
Zero-page	06
Absolute, X	1E
Zero-page, X	16

4. BRANCH ON CARRY CLEAR

Mnemonic BCC

Tests the carry flag. If clear, the program branches forward or backward by the number of bytes (not instructions) specified (maximum −128 or +127). If the carry flag is set, the next instruction in sequence is executed.

Note that the displacement is in fact added to the first instruction after BCC, so the possible maximum displacements are in fact +129 to −126.

No flags are affected.

Address mode is Relative only, opcode 90.

5. BRANCH ON CARRY SET

Mnemonic BCS

Tests the carry flag. If set, the program branches forward or backward by the specified displacement (see BCC). If clear,

the next instruction in sequence is executed.
No flags are affected.
Address mode Relative only, opcode B0.

6. BRANCH IF (LAST RESULT) EQUAL TO ZERO

Mnemonic BEQ

Tests the Z flag. If set, the program branches forward or backward by the specified displacement (see BCC). If clear, the next instruction in sequence is executed.
No flags are affected.
Address mode Relative only, opcode F0.

7. TEST MEMORY BITS AGAINST ACCUMULATOR

Mnemonic BIT

Performs logical AND between the specified memory location and the accumulator, but the result is discarded. The accumulator and memory contents are unchanged. The result of the comparison is indicated by the zero flag. It is set to 1 if the comparison fails, 0 if memory and accumulator are equal. In addition, the V flag is set equal to bit 6 of the memory data, and the N flag is set equal to bit 7.

This instruction is used to test a specific bit (or bits) of a memory location by loading the appropriate value, usually called a mask, into the accumulator. It is mostly used in I/O applications.

Flags affected are Z, N, V.

Address mode	Opcode
Absolute	2C
Zero-page	24

8. BRANCH ON MINUS

Mnemonic BMI

Tests the N flag. If N is set, the program branches forward or backward by the specified displacement (see BCC). If clear, the next instruction in sequence is executed. In general, this instruction is only appropriate when signed arithmetic is being performed.

No flags are affected.

Address mode Relative only, opcode 30.

9. BRANCH ON (LAST RESULT) NOT EQUAL TO ZERO

Mnemonic BNE

Tests the Z flag. If clear the program branches forward or backward by the specified displacement (see BCC). If set, the next instruction in sequence is executed.

No flags are affected.

Address mode Relative only, opcode D0.

10. BRANCH ON PLUS

Mnemonic BPL

Tests the N flag. If clear, the program branches forward or backward by the specified displacement (see BCC). If set, the next instruction in sequence is executed. In general, this instruction is only appropriate when signed arithmetic is being performed.

No flags are affected.

Address mode Relative only, opcode 10.

11. BREAK

Mnemonic BRK

This is in effect a software interrupt. The program counter and status register are saved on the stack, then PCL and PCH are set to the values in memory locations FFFE and FFFF respectively. The status register saved on the stack has the B flag set, to differentiate between a BRK and an IRQ.

Unlike an interrupt, PC+2 is saved. This is because BRK is assumed to be used to replace a 2-byte instruction. This may not be the case when BRK is used in program debugging, and a correction may be necessary.

Users of the BBC microcomputer and Acorn Electron should note that BRK is used in error handling, and cannot normally be used for other purposes in user-written machine code programs.

Only the B flag is affected.

Address mode Implied only, opcode 00.

12. BRANCH ON OVERFLOW CLEAR

Mnemonic BVC

Tests the V flag. If clear, the program branches forward or backward by the specified displacement (see BCC). If set, the next instruction in sequence is executed.

No flags are affected.

Address mode Relative only, opcode 50.

13. BRANCH ON OVERFLOW SET

Mnemonic BVS

Tests the overflow flag. If set, the program branches forward or backward by the specified displacement (see BCC). If clear, the next instruction in sequence is executed.

No flags are affected.

Address mode Relative only, opcode 70.

14. CLEAR CARRY FLAG

Mnemonic CLC

Clears the carry flag. This is to allow an addition without a carry, and is used before ADC.

Only the carry flag is affected.

Address mode Implied only, opcode 18.

15. CLEAR DECIMAL FLAG

Mnemonic CLD

Clears the decimal flag, so that future ADC and SBC operations are performed in binary mode. It is wise to include this instruction at the beginning of any binary arithmetic routines called from BASIC.

Only the D flag is affected.

Address mode Implied only, opcode D8.

16. CLEAR INTERRUPT FLAG

Mnemonic CLI

Enables interrupts. Interrupt handling routines must always clear this flag before returning to the program, or further interrupts will be lost.

Only the I flag is affected.

Address mode Implied only, opcode 58.

17. CLEAR OVERFLOW FLAG

Mnemonic CLV

Clears the overflow flag.

Only the V flag is affected.

Address mode Implied only, opcode B8.

18. COMPARE TO ACCUMULATOR

Mnemonic CMP

The contents of the specified memory or immediate data are subtracted from the accumulator. The result is discarded. Flags N, Z and C may be set, depending on whether the result is positive, zero, or negative. The contents of the accumulator and memory are unchanged.

If the result is zero, Z flag is set, otherwise reset.

N is set, but is reset if bit 7 of comparison result = 1.

C is set if the accumulator contents are equal to or larger than the data.

CMP is usually used before a branch instruction. Use BCC to detect if the accumulator is greater than the data, BEQ to detect if the accumulator is equal to the data, BCS to detect if the accumulator is equal to or greater than the data. To detect if the accumulator contents are greater than the data, it is necessary to use BEQ followed by BCS.

Flags affected are N, Z and C.

Address mode	Opcode
Absolute	CD
Zero-page	C5
Immediate	C9
Absolute, X	DD
Absolute, Y	D9
(Indirect, X)	C1
(Indirect, Y)	D1
Zero-page, X	D5

19. COMPARE TO X REGISTER

Mnemonic CPX

Subtracts the specified data from the contents of the X register. The result is discarded, and register and memory unchanged. The flags N, Z and C may be set, depending on the result. See CMP for details.

CPX is usually used before a branch. See CMP for appropriate tests, substituting the X register for the accumulator.

Flags affected are N, Z and C.

Address mode	Opcode
Absolute	EC
Zero-page	E4
Immediate	E0

20. COMPARE TO Y REGISTER

Mnemonic CPY

Subtracts the specified data from the Y register. The result is discarded, and the register and memory unchanged. The flags N, Z and C may be set, depending on the result. See CMP for details.

CPY is usually used before a branch. See CMP for appropriate tests, substituting the Y register for the accumulator.

Flags affected are N, Z and C.

Address mode	Opcode
Absolute	CC
Zero-page	C4
Immediate	C0

21. DECREMENT

Mnemonic DEC

Subtracts 1 from the contents of the specified memory location, storing the result in that location. If the contents are 0, the result will be FF (255 decimal).

Flags affected are N and Z.

Address mode	Opcode
Absolute	CE
Zero-page	C6
Absolute, X	DE
Zero-page, X	D6

22. DECREMENT X REGISTER

Mnemonic DEX

Decrements the contents of register X by 1. This allows the register to be used as a counter.

Flags affected are N and Z.

Address mode Implied only, opcode CA.

23. DECREMENT Y REGISTER

Mnemonic DEY

Decrements the contents register Y by 1. This allows the register to be used as a counter.

Flags affected are N and Z.

Address mode Implied only, opcode 88.

24. LOGIC EXCLUSIVE-OR

Mnemonic EOR

Exclusive-ORs the specified data with the accumulator, the result being placed in the accumulator.

Flags affected are N and Z.

Logical EOR operates according to the following rules:—

1 EOR 1 = 0
1 EOR 0 = 1
0 EOR 0 = 0

Address mode	Opcode
Absolute	4D
Zero-page	45
Immediate	49
Absolute, X	5D
Absolute, Y	59
(Indirect, X)	41
(Indirect, Y)	51
Zero-page, X	55

25. INCREMENT MEMORY

Mnemonic INC

Adds one to the contents of the specified memory location, storing the result in that location. If the contents is $FF (255 decimal), the result will be 0.

Flags affected are N and Z.

Address mode	Opcode
Absolute	EE
Zero-page	E6
Absolute, X	FE
Zero-page, X	F6

26. INCREMENT X REGISTER

Mnemonic INX

Increments the contents of the X register by 1. This allows the register to be used as a counter.

Flags affected are N and Z.

Address mode Implied only, opcode E8.

27. INCREMENT Y REGISTER

Mnemonic INY

Increments the contents of the Y register by 1. This allows the register to be used as a counter.

Flags affected are N and Z.

Address mode Implied only, opcode C8.

28. JUMP TO ADDRESS

Mnemonic JMP

Loads the address specified into the program counter, thus causing a jump in the sequence of program execution. The address may be absolute or indirect. This is the only instruction to allow straight indirection.

No flags are affected.

Address mode	Opcode
Absolute	4C
Indirect	6C

29. JUMP TO SUBROUTINE

Mnemonic JSR

Loads a new address into the program counter, causing a jump to that address, having first saved the current program position on the stack as a return address (see RTS). Note that it is the contents of the program counter +2 which is saved, this being the address of the next instruction after JSR.

No flags are affected.

Address mode Absolute only, opcode 20.

30. LOAD THE ACCUMULATOR

Mnemonic LDA

Loads the specified data into the accumulator.

Flags affected are N and Z.

Address mode	Opcode
Absolute	AD
Zero-page	A5
Immediate	A9
Absolute, X	BD
Absolute, Y	B9
(Indirect, X)	A1
(Indirect, Y)	B1
Zero-page, X	B5

31. LOAD THE X REGISTER

Mnemonic LDX

Loads the specified data into the X register.
Flags affected are N and Z.

Address mode	Opcode
Absolute	AE
Zero-page	A6
Immediate	A2
Absolute, Y	BE
Zero-page, Y	B6

32. LOAD THE Y REGISTER

Mnemonic LDA

Loads the specified data into the Y register.
Flags affected are N and Z.

Address mode	Opcode
Absolute	AC
Zero-page	A4
Immediate	A0
Absolute, X	BC
Zero-page, X	B4

33. LOGICAL SHIFT RIGHT

Mnemonic LSR

Shifts the contents of the accumulator or specified memory one bit position to the right. Result is stored in the source.

Bit 0 is stored in the carry flag. Bit 7 is set to 0.
Flags affected are N, Z and C.

Address mode	Opcode
Accumulator	4A
Absolute	4E
Zero-page	46
Absolute, X	5E
Zero-page, X	56

34. NO OPERATION

Mnemonic NOP

Does nothing, but takes up two machine cycles. May be used to pad a software timing loop, or to fill patches in a program.
No flags are affected.
Address mode Implied only, opcode EA.

35. INCLUSIVE OR WITH ACCUMULATOR

Mnemonic ORA

Logic inclusive-ORs the accumulator and specified data, the result being placed in the accumulator. May be used to force 1s at specified bit positions.

Inclusive-OR is performed according to the following rules:—

    1 OR 1 = 1
    1 OR 0 = 1
    0 OR 0 = 0

Flags affected are N and Z.

Address mode	Opcode
Absolute	0D
Zero-page	05
Immediate	09
Absolute, X	1D
Absolute, Y	19
(Indirect, X)	01
(Indirect, Y)	11
Zero-page, X	15

36. PUSH ACCUMULATOR ONTO STACK

Mnemonic PHA

Stores the contents of the accumulator on the stack, updating the stack pointer. Accumulator contents are unchanged.
No flags are affected.

Address mode Implied only, opcode 48.

37. PUSH PROCESSOR STATUS ONTO STACK

Mnemonic PHP

Stores the contents of the status register P on the stack and updates the stack pointer. P is unchanged.
No flags are affected.

Address mode Implied only, opcode 08.

38. PULL ACCUMULATOR FROM STACK

Mnemonic PLA

Loads the accumulator with the top word of the stack, and increments the stack pointer.
   Flags affected are N and Z.
   Address mode Implied only, opcode 68.

39. PULL PROCESSOR STATUS FROM STACK

Mnemonic PLP

Transfers the top word of the stack into the processor status register P, and increments the stack pointer.
   All flags are affected.
   Address mode Implied only, opcode 28.

40. ROTATE LEFT (one bit)

Mnemonic ROL

Rotates the contents of the specified address or accumulator left by one bit position. The carry flag is used as a ninth bit. The carry goes into bit 0, and bit 7 goes into the carry.
   Flags affected are N, Z and C.

Address mode	Opcode
Accumulator	2A
Absolute	2E
Zero-page	26
Absolute, X	3E
Zero-page, X	36

41. ROTATE RIGHT (one bit)

Mnemonic ROR

Rotates the contents of the specified address or accumulator right by one bit position. The carry flag is used as a ninth bit. The carry goes into bit 7, and bit 0 goes into the carry.

Flags affected are N, Z and C.

Address mode	Opcode
Accumulator	6A
Absolute	6E
Zero-page	66
Absolute, X	7E
Zero-page, X	76

42. RETURN FROM INTERRUPT

Mnemonic RTI

Restores the status register and program counter, which are saved on the stack when an interrupt occurs, and adjusts the stack pointer.

All flags are affected.

Address mode Implied only, opcode 40.

43. RETURN FROM SUBROUTINE

Mnemonic RTS

Restores the program counter from the stack (saved by JSR) and increments it by 1. Adjusts the stack pointer.

No flags are affected.

Address mode Implied only, opcode 60.

44. SUBTRACT WITH CARRY

Mnemonic SBC

Subtracts the specified data from the accumulator, with borrow. The result is placed in the accumulator. Will operate in either decimal or binary mode, depending on the D flag.
Flags affected are N, V, Z and C.

Address mode	Opcode
Absolute	ED
Zero-page	E5
Immediate	E9
Absolute, X	FD
Absolute, Y	F9
(Indirect, X)	E1
(Indirect, Y)	F1
Zero-page, X	F5

45. SET CARRY FLAG

Mnemonic SEC

Sets the carry flag to 1. This can be used before a SBC to subtract without a borrow.
Only the C flag is affected.
Address mode Implied only, opcode 38.

46. SET DECIMAL MODE FLAG

Mnemonic SED

Sets the decimal flag to 1. ADC and SBC will then be performed in BCD until a CLD is executed.
Only the D flag is affected.
Address mode Implied only, opcode F8.

47. SET INTERRUPT DISABLE FLAG

Mnemonic SEI

Sets the interrupt mask to 1. Used during interrupt service routines and system reset, or whenever interrupts cannot be allowed.

Only the I flag is affected.

Address mode Implied only, opcode 78.

48. STORE ACCUMULATOR IN MEMORY

Mnemonic STA

Stores a copy of the accumulator contents at the specified memory location. The accumulator is unchanged.

No flags are affected.

Address mode	Opcode
Absolute	8D
Zero-page	85
Absolute, X	9D
Absolute, Y	99
(Indirect, X)	81
(Indirect, Y)	91
Zero-page, X	95
Absolute	8E
Zero-page	86
Zero-page, Y	96

49. STORE X IN MEMORY

Mnemonic STX

Stores a copy of index register X at specified memory location. X is unchanged.
 No flags are affected.

50. STORE Y IN MEMORY

Mnemonic STY

Stores a copy of index register Y at specified memory location. Y is unchanged.
 No flags are affected.

Address mode	Opcode
Absolute	8C
Zero-page	84
Zero-page, X	94

51. TRANSFER ACCUMULATOR TO X

Mnemonic TAX

Copies the contents of the accumulator into index register X. The accumulator is unchanged.
 The N and Z flags are affected.
 Address mode Implied only, opcode AA.

52. TRANSFER ACCUMULATOR TO Y

Mnemonic TAY

Copies the contents of the accumulator into index register Y. The accumulator is unchanged.
 The N and Z flags are affected.
 Address mode Implied only, opcode A8.

53. TRANSFER STACK POINTER TO X

Mnemonic TSX

Copies the contents of the stack pointer into X. The stack pointer is unaltered.

The N and Z flags are affected.

Address mode Implied only, opcode BA.

54. TRANSFER X TO ACCUMULATOR

Mnemonic TXA

Copies the contents of the index register X into the accumulator. X is unchanged.

The N and Z flags are affected.

Address mode Implied only, opcode 8A.

55. TRANSFER X INTO STACK POINTER

Mnemonic TXS

Copies the contents of the index register X into the stack pointer S. X is unchanged.

No flags are affected.

Address mode implied only, opcode 9A.

56. TRANSFER Y INTO THE ACCUMULATOR

Mnemonic TYA

Copies the contents of index register Y into the accumulator. Y is unchanged.

Flags N and Z are affected.

Address mode Implied only, opcode 98.

Chapter 3

ADDRESSING MODES

Addressing is the means by which the processor determines, from the instruction, the location of the data, or operand, on which the instruction will operate. The 6502 has 9 possible address modes, though some of these have slight variants.

Most instructions can use more than one addressing mode. Though the same mnemonic is used, for all addressing modes, the opcode is obviously different. When an assembler is used, it will normally determine the address mode from the way the instruction is written. Special symbols or syntax are used to indicate some modes. When hand assembling, care must be taken to select the correct opcode, and to provide the correct number of bytes after the opcode. These may vary with a given instruction depending on the address mode in use.

Full use of the available address modes is important to good programming, and it is important to understand them thoroughly.

1. IMPLIED ADDRESSING

This mode of addressing is used only by instructions which operate on one or more of the 6502's internal registers without requiring external data. Some such operations may, however, require some external memory access, for example, the stack.

All these instructions are a single byte long.

Instructions using this mode are CLC, CLD, CLI, CLV, DEX, DEY, INX, INY, NOP, SEC, SED, SEI, TAX, TAY, TSX, TXA, TXS, TYA, and with memory access BRK, PHA, PHP, PLA, PLP, RTI, RTS.

2. IMMEDIATE ADDRESSING

In this mode, the operand is included in the program, immediately after the opcode. As the 6502 only has 8-bit registers, the operand can only occupy a single byte. All such instructions are therefore two bytes long. The hash symbol is used to indicate immediate mode, thus LDA#16 means load the accumulator with the value 16. This address mode allows constant data to be included within programs.

Instructions using this mode are ADC, AND, CMP, CPX, CPY, EOR, LDA, LDX, LDY, ORA, SBC.

3. ABSOLUTE ADDRESSING

In absolute addressing, the location of the operand in memory is specified in the instruction. Two bytes are used, so any position in the available 64k may be specified. This is the means by which variable data may be accessed by the program.

These instructions are three bytes long.

Instructions using this mode are ADC, AND, ASL, BIT, CMP, CPX, CPY, DEC, EOR, INC, JMP, JSR, LDA, LDX, LDY, LSR, ORA, ROL, ROR, SBC, STA, STX, STY.

4. ZERO PAGE

This is really a special case of absolute addressing. An 8-bit address follows the opcode, this being regarded as the low byte of the full 16-bit address, the upper byte being assumed to be zero. Thus, this mode can address only the first, zero, page of memory.

Zero page has special significance in 6502 programming. This special address mode allows it to be accessed faster than other pages of memory, and it is used virtually as extra registers for important variables and data which needs to be accessed frequently or at speed. You should reserve zero page for such purposes and not clutter it up with program code which could go anywhere in memory.

Care should be taken over the use of zero page when using machine code and a high level language, such as BASIC, together. Many zero page locations will be used by the high level language and if these are corrupted during machine code execution a machine crash is likely.

Instructions in this mode are two bytes long.

Instructions using this mode are ADC, AND, ASL, BIT, CMP, CPX, CPY, DEC, EOR, INC, LDA, LDX, LDY, LSR, ORA, ROL, ROR, SBC, STA, STX, STY.

5. RELATIVE ADDRESSING

With the 6502, this addressing mode is used only with branch instructions, and branch instructions only use relative mode.

In relative addressing, the byte following the instruction contains a displacement, which is regarded as a signed number between −128 and +127. If the program branches, this displacement is added to the contents of the program counter, causing a jump forwards or backwards. Note that the displacement is the number of memory locations, not the number of instructions.

With most assemblers, you specify the address of the memory location to which the program is to branch, and the assembler calculates the displacement for you.

All instructions using this mode are two bytes long.

This mode is only used by BCC, BCS, BEQ, BMI, BNE, BPL, BVC, BVS.

6. INDIRECT ADDRESSING

In indirect addressing, two bytes following the opcode contain a memory address. The contents of this address, and the byte that follows it, give a further address, which is where the data is to be found.

In fact, very few microprocessors allow indirect addressing, and the 6502 allows it only with one instruction, JMP. This is a three-byte instruction.

Indirect addressing is indicated by enclosing the second part of the instruction in brackets, thus JMP($0376) means that the program should jump to the instruction at the address given by the contents of the two bytes at $0376 and $0377.

The concept of indirection is an important one. Some people find it hard to grasp, but it is important that you do so, even if straight indirection is limited to one instruction with the 6502, as a form of indirection is widely used in programming.

INDEXED ADDRESSING

Indexed addressing, which may be combined with indirect addressing, means that the contents of one of the index registers, X and Y, are used to modify the address given or pointed to in the instruction. This makes it easy, using the increment or decrement instructions on the registers, to access a number of successive bytes of memory using a loop structure.

7. ABSOLUTE INDEXED ADDRESSING

In this mode, the contents of either the X or the Y register is added to the address contained in the instruction. In assembly language this is written as, for example, LDA $4800,X.

Using the X register, it is permissible to have either a 16-bit or an 8-bit (i.e. zero page) address. The Y register, however, can only be used with 16-bit addresses, with the exception of the instructions LDX and STX, which may be modified by the Y register.

The instructions which may be used with the X register are ADC, AND, ASL, CMP, DEC, EOR, INC, LDA, LDY, LSR, ORA, ROL, ROR, SBC, STA.

The instructions which may be used with the Y register are ADC, AND, CMP, EOR, LDA, LDX, ORA, SBC, STA.

Additionally, with zero page indexed addressing, STY may be used (with the X register only, of course).

8. INDIRECT INDEXED ADDRESSING

In this mode, the instruction contains an address of a memory location which, as it can only be one byte long, must be in zero page. The contents of this zero page location, plus the one following it, give an address anywhere in memory, to which the contents of the Y register (X cannot be used) are added to give the final address.

This address mode is used to access elements in a table. By saving the base address in zero page, the Nth element in the table can be accessed by loading N into the Y register. It is also easy to access sequential elements in the table by using a loop structure and the INY or DEY instructions.

This address mode also provides a way of accessing more than 256 bytes of memory sequentially, by incrementing or decrementing the high byte of the address in zero page after each 256 bytes.

In assembly language, this mode is indicated by putting the zero page address in brackets, followed by the index register. For example, STA ($00D0),Y.

The only instructions which can use this mode are ADC, AND, CMP, EOR, LDA, ORA, SBC, STA.

9. INDEXED INDIRECT ADDRESSING

In this mode, the instruction again contains an address in zero page, but this time the contents of the X register (Y cannot be used) is added to the zero page address. The contents of this byte plus the one following it give the address where the final data are to be found. In other words, the indirection occurs one stage earlier than in indirect indexed addressing.

This mode is used to pick out elements of a table of addresses stored in zero page. The base address of the table is contained in the instruction, and to access element N, 2N is loaded into the X register.

In assembly language, this mode is indicated by including the zero-page address and index register in brackets. For example, LDA ($0070,X).

This address mode is unlikely to be of great use. The instructions which can use this mode are ADC, AND, CMP, EOR, LDA, ORA, SBC, STA.

Chapter 4

STORING AND EXECUTION

The home computers with which this book is primarily concerned all have BASIC in ROM as their main language. BASIC normally expects to be able to use all the user area of memory either for program storage or for variables.

In order to use machine code in these computers it is necessary to either find some way of protecting the code from being overwritten by BASIC, or to store the code in odd corners of the memory map which are normally not used either by BASIC or by the operating system.

The BBC micro and its close relative the Acorn Electron are the most helpful in this respect. Not only do they have built-in assemblers as part of the BASIC language interpreter, but they also have a special version of the DIM statement to reserve a block of memory. This takes the form DIM START 50. This reserves a block of 51 bytes, the address of the first byte being stored in the variable START. START could be any legal BASIC variable name. This method of code storage is so easy and straightforward that it is not usually worth considering other methods with these computers.

With the Atari, ORIC-1 and Atmos, Commodore 64 and VIC-20, no such in-built method exists. With these computers, different approaches are necessary depending on whether only a short routine or a longer machine code program is to be stored.

With short routines, a very simple method of storage is to use a REM at the very beginning of the program. This can initially be filled with any character. The machine code is then POKEd into the area of memory occupied by these characters either from DATA statements when the program is run, or directly from command mode a byte at a time. The byte at a time method is time consuming, but worthwhile on a computer like the VIC-20, which has a very small memory in its basic form.

The advantage of the REM method is that, when the program is recorded on disc or tape, the machine code in the REM is recorded with it. The length of the code is, however, limited to the length of a BASIC line, about 70 characters on these computers. Though not impossible to split code between two or more REMs, it is very difficult.

The REM must be at the start of the program, both to make it easy to locate, and to prevent it moving if the BASIC program is edited.

Odd corners of memory tend not to be very satisfactory. For a start, they tend to be very small, perhaps 10 or 20 bytes. Secondly, computer manufacturers tend to modify their products from time to time, sometimes unannounced, and an unused corner can suddenly find employment. This means that a program using this storage method may not work on all versions of a machine. A good example of the problems which can arise is with the ORIC-1. This has 20 (hex) bytes of memory free at the start of page 4 of memory. Examples using this area are given in the user manual. However, if you buy the ORICMON machine code monitor program, it uses the whole of page 4 as its input buffer, which makes it hard to store routines there!

The best method of storing substantial machine code programs is to store them above the area used by BASIC. To do this, the area used by BASIC must be reduced, by lowering the highest memory location available to BASIC. The address of this location is stored in RAM, and is given a name, such as HIMEM or MEMTOP.

In the BBC computer and Electron, HIMEM is a pseudo-variable name recognised by BASIC. It can therefore easily be altered to any required value, by, for example, the statement HIMEM=&2500, and PRINT HIMEM will give the current value.

The ORIC also recognises HIMEM, but for assignment only, and the equals sign is not used. Thus you can use HIMEM #9000, but not PRINT HIMEM. The current value can be found by PRINT DEEK #A6.

Atari prefer the name MEMTOP, but this is not recognised

by the computer. Instead, it is necessary to PEEK or POKE the appropriate memory locations, which are 741 and 742 (decimal). The high byte is first, as usual, so PEEK(741)+256*PEEK(742) will give the current value (the highest actual address is one less than this).

Just to be different, Commodore use the label MEMSIZ, and, like the Atari, this is not recognised by the computer. The locations to PEEK and POKE are 55 and 56 (decimal).

It must be borne in mind that these memory locations are liable to be reset by the operating system if the BREAK or RESET key is pressed, or if the display mode is changed.

EXECUTION

Putting the machine code in memory is the first step. The second is to cause it to be executed. Whether in a program or from command mode, this normally has to be done with a BASIC statement.

The simplest statement to use is CALL, which exists in the BBC/Electron and in the ORIC BASICs. Commodore BASIC has a similar command SYS. These commands are followed by the start address of the machine code routine. The routine must be terminated by an RTS instruction (not matched to a JSR within the routine) to cause a return to BASIC. Thus CALL START will execute a machine code routine starting at an address stored in the variable START in the BBC/Electron or ORIC, and SYS 2054 will execute a machine code routine starting at address 2054 decimal (this would be one stored in a REM on the Commodore 64).

The BBC/Electron CALL statement allows a variable number of parameters to be passed to the machine code routine, but a discussion of this is beyond the scope of this introductory book.

The alternative statement is USR. This executes a machine-code routine which is supposed to return a floating-point value to the program, which is deposited in a variable or printed. This is the only statement available to execute machine code in the Atari computer. However, it is possible to use this statement to execute any machine code program, by using a dummy variable to take the (non-existent) result. This statement takes the general form A=USR(AAAA), where AAAA is the start address. The USR statement varies considerably from computer to computer (in particular, the Atari has provision for optional parameter passing) and reference to your computer's manual for details is advised. Generally, return to BASIC is again by an RTS instruction.

Chapter 5

EXAMPLE PROGRAMS

The short demonstration programs in this chapter will be given in standard 3-column assembly language form. The first column contains labels of memory locations, to which branch and jump instructions may refer. The second column contains the operation mnemonics, and the third column the operand.

BASIC listings to enable the programs to be entered and run on several popular 6502 based home computers are also given. In the case of the BBC computer and Electron, these use the in built assembler. In other cases, the machine code is loaded from DATA statements.

If you have an assembler for your computer, you should be able to enter the programs from the assembly language listings.

ADD

```
START       LDA       NUM1L
            CLC
            ADC       NUM2L
            STA       RESL
            LDA       NUM1H
            ADC       NUM2H
            STA       RESH
```

This program adds together two 16-bit numbers. The result will only be correct if it does not exceed 65535. The numbers to be added are stored in memory locations which we call NUM1H,NUM1L, and NUM2H,NUM2L, that is, high and low bytes of the two numbers respectively.

The low byte of the first number is placed in the accumulator. The carry flag is cleared. The low byte of the second number is added to the accumulator contents, and the result is stored in a memory location which we call RESL.

67

The high byte of the first number is then loaded into the accumulator. This time any carry from the low bytes must be added in, so the carry flag is not cleared. The high byte of the second number is added, and the result stored in RESH. This completes the operation.

The memory location used for the storage of the numbers and result could be anywhere in memory, but in the listings given I have used 6 bytes immediately before the machine code routine.

TAKE

```
START       LDA         NUM1L
            SEC
            SBC         NUM2L
            STA         DIFFL
            LDA         NUM1H
            SBC         NUM2H
            STA         DIFFH
```

It can be seen that this routine is very similar to the addition routine in structure. However, this time, after loading the low byte of the first number into the accumulator, the carry flag is set, rather than cleared, as we do not want a borrow at this stage. The carry flag is not set for the high byte subtraction, as any borrow is relevant. Note that the listings as given cannot cope with the second number being larger than the first, i.e. a negative result.

Note that the only address mode used in these programs is Absolute (apart from CLC and SBC which use implied addressing) and there are no branch instructions.

LOOP

```
START     LDX      #0
          LDA      #0
          STA      $70
          STA      $71
LOOP      INX
          TXA
          CLC
          ADC      $70
          STA      $70
          BCC      OVER
          INC      $71
OVER      CPX      #255
BNE       LOOP
```

This is an example of loop structure, and is equivalent to the following BASIC program.

```
10  FOR X=1 TO 255
20  T=T+X
30  NEXT X
```

It is interesting to run both programs and compare the time taken. The BASIC version takes from about half a second (BBC computer) to nearly 5 seconds (VIC-20). The machine code version is virtually instantaneous.

The X register is used as the equivalent of the control variable to count the number of loops. It is initially set to 0. Two zero page locations are used to hold the total, and these too are initially set to 0. Zero page is used here for speed, always worthwhile in loops with many cycles. (The zero page locations given are as used in the BBC and Electron listings, different locations are used for other computers.) At the start of the loop, the X register is incremented. The X register contents is then transferred to the accumulator, and added to the low byte of the total. If there is a carry from this addition, the high byte is incremented. If the carry flag is clear, this instruction is jumped over. Using a branch and an increment instruction in this way is faster than the alternative of using LDA #0:ADC NUMH:STA NUMH. The contents of the X register is then compared to 255. If this value has not been reached, the program branches back to LOOP. Otherwise it terminates.

This program has been written to model the BASIC version as closely as possible. In general, in machine code, it is easier to count down in loops than to count up. Try changing the beginning to LDX #255, take out the INX, and change the CPX #255 to DEX. It can be seen that this saves an instruction, and is consequently faster.

This program uses a forward branch, so in the BBC/Electron listing, two pass assembly is used.

TIMES

START	LDA	#1
	STA	CHECK
	LDX	#8
LOOP	LDA	MULT
	AND	CHECK
	BNE	ADD
	BEQ	ROUND
ADD	LDA	NUM
	CLC	
	ADC	RESL
	STA	RESL
	LDA	NUMH
	ADC	RESH
	STA	RESH
ROUND	ASL	NUMH
	ASL	NUM
	BCC	OVER

```
                    INC        NUMH
        OVER        ASL        CHECK
                    DEX
                    BNE        LOOP
```

This program multiplies together two 8-bit numbers, yielding a 16-bit result.

Binary multiplication is performed by shifting and adding. If you shift the bits of a binary number one place to the left, inserting a zero on the right, the number is multiplied by two. To multiply two numbers together, the following method is used. We will call the two numbers Number and Multiplier. If bit 0 of the Multiplier is set, Number is added to the result. Number is then shifted one bit to the left. If bit 1 of Multiplier is set then Number (shifted) is again added to the result. This is repeated until all the bits of Multiplier have been tested.

To perform this in practice, a loop structure is used. 1 is loaded into a byte in memory which I have called CHECK. 8 is loaded into the X register. The multiplier is loaded into the accumulator, and is ANDed with CHECK to see if bit 0 is set.

If it is, a two-byte addition is performed, adding NUM and NUMH to RESL and RESH.

If it is not, the program branches to ROUND (and this part of the program is also performed after each addition). The two bytes of NUM are shifted to the left. If a carry is generated when the low byte is shifted, it is added into the high byte by using INC. CHECK is also shifted left. The X register is decremented. When it reaches zero, all 8 bits have been checked, and the routine terminates.

You will have noted that although NUM is an 8-bit number to begin with, two bytes have to be reserved for it, to allow for the 8 stages of shift performed on it.

These simple programs are just intended to give a brief introduction to some of the principles of machine code programming. The only way to learn how to program is to program. It is intended that you will use these routines as jumping boards for your own experiments. In particular, try to extend the programs to cope with 3 and 4 byte numbers, and the loop program to cope with more than 256 cycles (Hint: Use both index registers).

Experimenting with machine code may cause more frequent (and sometimes more spectacular) crashes than experimenting with BASIC, but remember, nothing you can type in at the keyboard can do any permanent harm to your computer. All you can lose is your typing.

NOTE ON THE BBC/ELECTRON LISTINGS

At the beginning of the assembler parts of three of these listings you will see labels followed by a BRK instruction. This is a simple method of reserving bytes for variable storage. The instructions are just dummys and are never executed. BRK is chosen because it has the opcode 0. An alternative, which will work with the Electron and the most recent version of the British Broadcasting Corporation microcomputer (as it is now officially called) is as follows:—

```
OLD:  50.NUML:BRK
NEW:  50.NUML:EQUB 0
```

This will not work with versions of the BBC computer using BASIC 1 as the pseudo-operations EQUB, EQUD, EQUW, and EQUS are not supported.

MACHINE SPECIFIC LISTINGS

BBC/Electron Versions

ADD

```
0 REM ."ADD"
0 REM BBC/ELECTRON version
0 DIM STORE 50
0 P%=STORE
0[.NUM1H:BRK
0.NUM1L:BRK
0.NUM2H:BRK
0.NUM2L:BRK
0.RESH:BRK
0.RESL:BRK
0.START
0LDA NUM1L
0 CLC
0 ADC NUM2L
0 STA RESL
0 LDA NUM1H
0 ADC NUM2H
0 STA RESH
0 RTS:]
0 INPUT"FIRST NUMBER",N1
0 INPUT"SECOND NUMBER",N2
0 ?NUM1H=N1 DIV 256:?NUM1L=N1 MOD 256
0 ?NUM2H=N2 DIV 256:?NUM2L=N2 MOD 256
0 CALLSTART
0 PRINT 256*?RESH+?RESL
0 GOTO 200
```

TAKE

```
  10 REM "TAKE"
  20 REM BBC/ELECTRON version
  30 DIM STORE 50
  40 P%=STORE
  50[.NUM1H:BRK
  60.NUM1L:BRK
  70.NUM2H:BRK
  80.NUM2L:BRK
  90.DIFFH:BRK
 100.DIFFL:BRK
 110.START
 120 LDA NUM1L
 130 SEC
 140 SBC NUM2L
 150 STA DIFFL
 160 LDA NUM1H
 170 SBC NUM2H
 180 STA DIFFH
 190 RTS:]
 200 INPUT"FIRST NUMBER",N1
 210 INPUT"SECOND NUMBER",N2
 220 ?NUM1H=N1 DIV 256:?NUM1L=N1 MOD 25
 230 ?NUM2H=N2 DIV 256:?NUM2L=N2 MOD 25
 240 CALLSTART
 250 PRINT 256*?DIFFH+?DIFFL
 260 GOTO 200
```

74

```
10   REM "LOOP"
20   REM BBC/ELECTRON version
30   DIM START 50
40   FOR I%=0 TO 2 STEP 2
50   P%=START
60   COPT I%
70   .START
80   LDX #0
90   LDA #0
100  STA &70
110  STA &71
120  .LOOP
130  INX
140  TXA
150  CLC
160  ADC &70
170  STA &70
180  BCC OVER
190  INC &71
200  .OVER
210  CPX #255
220  BNE LOOP
230  RTS:]
240  NEXT I%
250  CALLSTART
260  PRINT256*?&71+?&70
```

```
 10 REM "TIMES"
 20 REM BBC/ELECTRON version
 30 DIM STORE 70
 40 FOR L=0 TO 3 STEP 3
 50 P%=STORE
 60[OPT L
 70 .NUM:BRK
 80 .NUMH:BRK
 90 .MULT:BRK
100 .CHECK:BRK
110 .RESH:BRK
120.RESL:BRK
130.START
140 LDA #I
150 STA CHECK
160 LDX #8
170.LOOP
180 LDA MULT
190 AND CHECK
200 BNE ADD
210 BEQ ROUND
220.ADD
230 LDA NUM
240 CLC
250 ADC RESL
260 STA RESL
270 LDA NUMH
280 ADC RESH
290 STA RESH
300.ROUND
310 ASL NUMH
320 ASL NUM
330 BCC OVER
```

```
340 INC NUMH
350.OVER
360 ASL CHECK
370 DEX
380 BNE LOOP
390 RTS:]
400 NEXT L
410 INPUT"FIRST NUMBER",?NUM
420 INPUT"SECOND NUMBER",?MULT
430 CALLSTART
440 PRINT 256*?RESH+?RESL
450 ?RESH=0:?RESL=0:?NUMH=0
460 GOTO 410
```

ADD

```
10 REM "ADD"
20 REM VIC-20 VERSION
30 POKE 55,0:POKE 56,29
40 FOR M=7611 TO 7630
50 READ V
60 POKE M,V
70 NEXT M
80 DATA 173,181,29,24,109,183,29
,141,185,29
90 DATA 173,180,29,109,182,29,14
1,184,29,96
100 INPUT"FIRST NUMBER";N1
110 INPUT"SECOND NUMBER";N2
120 FH=INT(N1/256):POKE 7604,FH
130 FL=N1-256*FH:POKE 7605,FL
140 SH=INT(N1/256):POKE 7606,SH
150 SL=N2-256*SH:POKE 7607,SL
160 SYS 7611
170 PRINT 256*PEEK(7608)+PEEK(760
9)
180 GOTO 100
```

TAKE

```
   10 REM "TAKE"
   20 REM VIC-20 VERSION
   30 POKE 55,0:POKE 56,29
   40 FOR M=7618 TO 7637
   50 READ V
   60 POKE M,V
   70 NEXT M
   80 DATA 173,189,29,56,237,191,29
,141,193,29
   90 DATA 173,188,29,237,190,29,14
1,192,29,96
  100 INPUT"FIRST NUMBER";N1
  110 INPUT"SECOND NUMBER";N2
  120 FH=INT(N1/256):POKE 7612,FH
  130 FL=N1-256*FH:POKE 7613,FL
  140 SH=INT(N2/256):POKE 7614,SH
  150 SL=N2-256*SH:POKE 7615,SL
  160 SYS 7618
  170 PRINT 256*PEEK(7616)+PEEK(761
7)
  180 GOTO 100
```

```
10 REM "LOOP"
20 REM VIC-20 VERSION
30 POKE 55,0:POKE 56,29
40 FOR M=7424 TO 7447
50 READ V
60 POKE M,V
70 NEXT M
80 DATA 162,0,169,0,133,251,133,
252,232,138,24,101,251,133,251
90 DATA 144,2,230,252,224,255,20
8,241,96
100 SYS 7424
110 PRINT 256*PEEK(252)+PEEK(251)
```

TIMES

```
   10 REM "TIMES"
   20 REM VIC-20 VERSION
   30 POKE 55,0:POKE 56,29
   40 FOR M=7552 TO 7611
   50 READ V
   60 POKE M,V
   70 NEXT M
   80 DATA 0,0,0,0,0,0,169,1,141,13
1,29,162,8,173,130,29,45,131,29
   90 DATA 208,2,240,19,173,128,29,
24,109,133,29,141,133,29,173,129,29
  100 DATA 109,132,29,141,132,29,14
,129,29,14,128,29,144,3,238,129,29
  110 DATA 14,131,29,202,208,210,96
  120 INPUT"FIRST NUMBER";NUM
  130 INPUT"SECOND NUMBER";MULT
  140 POKE 7552,NUM
  150 POKE 7554,MULT
  160 SYS 7558
  170 PRINT 256*PEEK(7556)+PEEK(755
7)
  180 FOR M=7552 TO 7557:POKE M,0:N
EXT
  190 GOTO 120
```

ADD

```
10 REM "ADD"
20 REM C-64 VERSION
30 POKE 55,0:POKE 56,143
40 FOR M=36795 TO 36814
50 READ V
60 POKE M,V
70 NEXT M
80 DATA 173,181,143,24,109,183,1
43,141,185,143,173,180,143,109,182,
143,141,184
90 DATA 143,96
100 INPUT"FIRST NUMBER";N1
110 INPUT"SECOND NUMBER";N2
120 FH=INT(N1/256):POKE 36788,FH
130 FL=N1-256*FH:POKE 36789,FL
140 SH=INT(N2/256):POKE 36790,SH
150 SL=N2-256*SH:POKE 36791,SL
160 SYS 36795
170 PRINT 256*PEEK(36792)+PEEK(36
793)
180 GOTO 100
```

```
10 REM "TAKE"
20 REM C-64 VERSION
30 POKE 55,0:POKE 56,143
40 FOR M=36802 TO 36821
50 READ V
60 POKE M,V
70 NEXT M
80 DATA 173,189,143,56,237,191,1
43,141,193,143,173,188,143,237,190,
143
90 DATA 141,192,143,96
100 INPUT"FIRST NUMBER";N1
110 INPUT"SECOND NUMBER";N2
120 FH=INT(N1/256):POKE 36796,FH
130 FL=N1-256*FH:POKE 36797,FL
140 SH=INT(N2/256):POKE 36798,SH
150 SL=N2-256*SH:POKE 36799,SL
160 SYS 36802
170 PRINT 256*PEEK(36800)+PEEK(36
801)
180 GOTO 100
```

```
10 REM "LOOP"
20 REM C-64 VERSION
30 POKE 55,0:POKE 56,143
40 FOR M=36608 TO 36631
50 READ V
60 POKE M,V
70 NEXT M
80 DATA 162,0,169,0,133,251,133,
252,232,138,24,101,251,133,251
90 DATA 144,2,230,252,224,255,20
8,241,96
100 SYS 36608
110 PRINT 256*PEEK(252)+PEEK(251)
```

TIMES

```
10 REM "TIMES"
20 REM C-64 VERSION
30 POKE 55,0:POKE 56,128
40 FOR M=32896 TO 32955
50 READ V
60 POKE M,V
70 NEXT M
80 DATA0,0,0,0,0,0,169,1,141,131
,128,162,8,173,130,128,45,131,128
90 DATA 208,2,240,19,173,128,128
,24,109,133,128,141,133,128,173,129
,128
100 DATA 109,132,128,141,132,128,
14,129,128,14,128,128,144,3,238,129
,128
110 DATA 14,131,128,202,208,210,9
6
120 INPUT"FIRST NUMBER";NUM
130 INPUT"SECOND NUMBER";MULT
140 POKE 32896,NUM
150 POKE 32898,MULT
160 SYS 32902
170 PRINT 256*PEEK(32900)+PEEK(32
901)
180 FOR M=32896 TO 32901:POKE M,0
:NEXT
190 GOTO 120
```

85

ADD

```
10 REM "ADD"

20 REM ORIC-1 version

30 HIMEM #8F00

40 FOR M=#8F6A TO #8FCD

50 READ V

60 POKE M,V

70 NEXT M

80 DATA #AD,#B5,#8F,#18,#6D
,#B7,#8F,#8D,#B9,#8F,#AD,#B
4,#8F,#6D,#B6,#8F

90 DATA #8D,#B8,#8F,#60

100 INPUT"FIRST NUMBER";N1

110 INPUT"SECOND NUMBER";N2

130 FH=INT(N1/256):POKE #8F
B4,FH
```

86

```
140 FL=N1-256*FH:POKE #8FB5
,FL
150 SL=INT(N2/256):POKE #8F
B6,SL
160 SL=N2-256*SH:POKE #8FB7
,SL
170 CALL #8FBA
180 PRINT 256*PEEK(#8FB8)+P
EEK(#8FB9)
190 GOTO 100
```

TAKE
```
10 REM "TAKE"
20 REM ORIC-1 version
30 HIMEM #8F00
40 FOR M=#8FC2 TO #8FD5
50 READ V
60 POKE M,V
70 NEXT M
```

```
80 DATA #AD,#BD,#8F,#38,#ED
,#BF,#8F,#8D,#C1,#8F,#AD,#B
C,#8F,#ED,#BE,#8F
90 DATA #8D,#C0,#8F,#60
100 INPUT"FIRST NUMBER";N1
110 INPUT"SECOND NUMBER";N2
120 FH=INT(N1/256):POKE #8F
BC,FH
130 FL=N1-256*FH:POKE #8FBD
,FL
140 SH=INT(N2/256):POKE #8F
BE,SH
150 SL=N2-256*SH:POKE #8FBF
,SL
160 CALL #8FC2
170 PRINT 256*PEEK(#8FC0)+P
EEK(#8FC1)
180 GOTO 100
```

```
10 REM "LOOP"
20 REM ORIC-1 version
30 HIMEM #F00
40 FOR M=#8F3C TO #8F53
50 READ V
60 POKE M,V
70 NEXT M
80 DATA #A2,0,#A9,0,#85,#70
,#85,#71,#E8,#8A,#18,#65,#7
0,#85,#70,#90,#02
90 DATA #E6,#71,#E0,#FF,#D0
,#F1,#60
100 CALL #8F3C
110 PRINT DEEK(#70)
```

TIMES

```
10 REM "TIMES"

20 REM ORIC-1 version

30 HIMEM #8000

40 FOR M=#8080 TO #80BB

50 READ V

60 POKE M,V

70 NEXT M

75 DATA 0,0,0,0,0,0

80 DATA #A9,#01,#8D,#83,#80
,#A2,#08,#AD,#82,#80,#2D,#8
3,#80,#D0,#02,#F0,#13

90 DATA #AD,#80,#80,#18,#6D
,#85,#80,#8D,#85,#80,#AD,#8
1,#80,#6D,#84,#80

100 DATA #8D,#84,#80
```

```
110 DATA #0E,#81,#80,#0E,#8
0,#80,#90,#03,#EE,#81,#80,#
0E,#83,#80,#CA
120 DATA #D0,#D2,#60
130 INPUT"FIRST NUMBER";NUM
140 INPUT"SECOND NUMBER";MU
LT
150 POKE #8080,NUM
160 POKE #8082,MULT
170 CALL #8086
180 PRINT 256*PEEK(#8084)+P
EEK(#8085)
190 FOR M=#8080 TO #8085:PO
KE M,0:NEXT
200 GOTO 130
```

Chapter 6

INPUT/OUTPUT

When using a high level language such as BASIC, commands to control input/output devices such as the CRT controller and printer port are normally provided, or they may be included in the form of operating system commands. In either case the user is not directly accessing registers of the input/output devices, and is unlikely to need any knowledge of the way in which they function. The situation is totally different with machine code, and in order to take advantage of the speed of machine code programs it is often necessary to directly access and control input/output circuits. This can be a little difficult at first, even for someone who is used to dealing with electronic circuits, since the methods adopted in computer peripherals are rather different to those used in non-computer electronic circuits. However, once a few fundamental points have been grasped it is not too difficult to use and understand practically any computer peripheral device.

Even just restricting ourselves to peripherals for use with the 6502, there are a number of devices in common use, and it would not be feasible to even briefly describe a few of these here due to the complexity of these components. Fortunately, the basic way in which these devices are controlled varies little from one type to another, and by taking a brief look at just one or two computer peripherals some important and universal points can be unveiled.

THE 6522

As an example of a peripheral integrated circuit we will consider the 6522. This has been chosen as it is to be found in several 6502 based home-computers (including such machines as the BBC A and B, the ORIC-1 and Atmos, and the VIC-20), and in many ways it is a fairly simple device (although only in relation to other computer peripherals which run the full gamut from complex to extremely complex)! The fact that these devices have very complicated circuits should not deter you, since to the programmer they appear to be relatively straightforward, and much of the complexity is not apparent. This is in much the same way that a microprocessor has an almost unbelievable array of electronics internally, but as far as the programmer is concerned it appears to be just an array of registers, as shown in Figure 1 and discussed earlier in this book.

Figure 5 gives pinout details of the 6522, which is a form of parallel interface adaptor, or PIA as these are more usually termed. A device of this type is used to get parallel data into and out of the microprocessor. By parallel data we simply mean that it normally transfers data in complete bytes, or perhaps in nibbles if a full byte of data is not required. The alternative is serial data where data is transferred one bit at a time (usually commencing with the least significant bit and ending with the most significant one). Parallel data transfer is the quicker and simpler method, and is the one normally used for data transfer within a computer. Serial data is restricted mainly to communications between one computer and another, or between a computer and a piece of peripheral equipment such as a printer or cassette recorder. Here the lesser number of connecting wires (as little as two can be used) and the fact that the system will work over long distances outweighs the slowness and relative complexity of serial data transfers. Serial data transmission and reception can actually be handled by the microprocessor using a suitable software routine and a very simple hardware interface, but it is more usually handled by a special interface device. These are known by a variety of names such as UARTs (universal asyncronous receiver/transmitters) and ASCIAs (asyncronous serial communications interface adaptors).

Returning to the 6522, the chip manufacturers refer to this as a VIA (versatile interface adaptor) rather than a PIA, as it has a few features in addition to its two parallel input/output

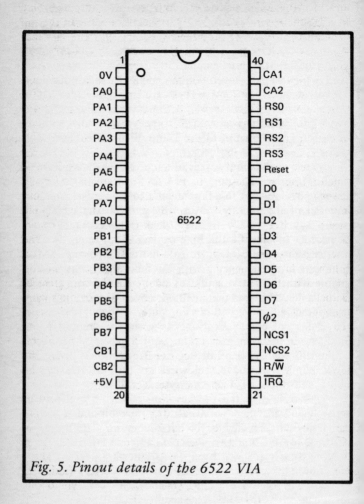

Fig. 5. Pinout details of the 6522 VIA

ports. These are two 16-bit counter/timers and a serial shift register. The latter can be used for serial data transmission and reception, but it is extremely basic when compared to a device such as a UART, and is of much less practical value than one might expect.

Looking at the pinouts of the 6522 you will notice pins marked NCS1 and NCS2. These are chip select pins, and in order to communicate with the device the microprocessor must take NCS1 high and NCS2 low. Normally these pins are driven from the twelve most significant address lines via a suitable decoder, so that the chip is enabled when any address in a block of sixteen consecutive addresses are accessed by the microprocessor. The pins marked RS0 to RS3 are the register select pins, and are usually fed direct from the four least significant address lines. By setting these at the appropriate states any one of the 6522's sixteen 8-bit registers can be accessed. In other words, by using suitable address decoding the registers are placed in the desired block of sixteen addresses in the memory map. The following list gives names of the sixteen registers and gives example addresses (these are actually the addresses for one of the two 6522s in the VIC-20 computer).

Address	Register
37136	Peripheral Register B
37137	Peripheral Register A
37138	Data Direction Register B
37139	Data Direction Register A
37140	Timer 1 low byte
37141	Timer 1 high byte
37142	Timer 1 counter low byte
37143	Timer 1 counter high byte
37144	Timer 2 low byte
37145	Timer 2 high byte
37146	Shift Register
37147	Auxiliary Control Register
37148	Peripheral Control Register
37149	Interrupt Flag Register

37150   Interrupt Enable Register
37151   Peripheral Register A (no handshaking)

The basic function of the 6522 is to provide two 8-bit input/output ports, and these are named Port A and Port B by the manufacturer. These are pins PA0 to PA7 and PB0 to PB7 of Figure 5. The ports are connected to the data bus via pins D0 to D7, so that the microprocessor can read from them or write to them. The R/W line is operated from the corresponding line of the microprocessor so that the 6522 is placed in the appropriate mode. If we wish to read (say) Port A, using BASIC it would just be a matter of PEEKing address 37137 (Peripheral Register A, or Port A in other words). Using machine code things are equally straightforward, and the LDA instruction would be used to read the contents of Port A and transfer it to the accumulator. PA0 corresponds to D0 of the data bus, PA1 corresponds to D1, and so on. Thus, if PA0 to PA3 were set high, and PA4 to PA7 were set low, the number transferred to the accumulator would be 00001111 in binary, or 15 in decimal.

Things are also reasonably simple if we wish to write to the port. The first task is to set the lines of Port A as outputs, and the lines are controlled in this respect by data direction register A at address 37139. Like the peripheral register, each bit of this register corresponds to one of the lines of Port A. Setting a bit low designates the relevant line as an input, while setting it high designates the line as an output. At switch-on a negative pulse is supplied to the reset pin of the 6522 (and also to many other chips in the computer including the 6502), and this pulse sets all the 6522's registers at 0. The lines of the two ports therefore all start off as inputs. To set Port A as an 8-bit output, 11111111 in binary (255 in decimal) is written to data direction register A. Using BASIC this would be:—

POKE 37139,255

The machine code/assembly language equivalent of this is:—

```
LDA 255
STA 37139
```

As each line can be individually set as an input or an output it is possible to have some lines as inputs and some as outputs, and the eight lines could be used with eight entirely separate items of peripheral equipment. However, care has to be taken if this is done as it is only possible to write to all 8 bits and to read all 8 bits. There is no problem in writing to bits that are set as inputs – the 6522 will just ignore data written to these.

When reading a port (or any register for that matter) the logic AND function can be used to mask any bits that are not of interest. For example, if only bits 6 and 7 are of interest, these bits represent 64 and 128 when set high, giving a total of 192. The accumulator is therefore loaded with 192, and the data at the port is then logic ANDed with this. With the logic AND instruction a bit of the accumulator will only be set at 1 if that bit was 1 in both of the ANDed numbers. Bits 0 to 5 were set at 0 when 192 was loaded into the accumulator, and these must be 0 in the answer. On the other hand, bits 6 and 7 were set at 1, and will be 1 in the answer if the corresponding bits of the data read from the port are also 1. Thus the required masking is obtained, with the unwanted bits being set at 0, and the bits of interest being set at the state read from the port.

There is more than one way of writing data to one bit of a port or register without affecting the states of the other bits, but the use of logic operations is probably the easiest. For instance, assume we wish to set bit 2 of a register to logic 1. All that we need to do is to place 4 in the accumulator (bit 2 high and all the others low), then logic OR the number returned from the port with this. With the logic OR function a bit is set at 1 if there is a 1 in that bit of the first number OR the second number OR both. Therefore, bits 0, 1, and 3 to 7 will remain unaltered, but bit 2 will be set high. The number in the accumulator is then transferred to the port.

The situation is equally straightforward if a bit must be set low, and if we assume that bit 2 is to be set low this time, we must first logic AND the number at the port with 251 (11111011 in binary). This ensures that bit 2 is set low, but the other bits will be unaffected. The number in the accumulator is then written to the port using the STA instruction.

CONTROL REGISTER

Peripheral devices normally have at least one control register, and may have several. The data direction register is actually a very simple form of control register, but most are somewhat more complex than this. The peripheral control register of the 6522 is a fairly typical example. We will not consider this register in detail, but will briefly consider just one section of it.

Bits 5 to 7 control line CB2 of the device. CB2 is a handshake line, and its primary purpose is to control the flow of data into or out of Port B. For example, CB2 could be set to the pulse mode, and it then acts as an output which gives a brief negative pulse each time data is written to Port B. This could be used to indicate to a piece of peripheral equipment that fresh data is present at the port and must be acted upon. Alternatively, CB2 could be used as an input, with the peripheral equipment indicating via this input when it has finished processing the last byte of data and is ready to process the next byte. CB2 has four input modes and four output modes, with whichever of these is required being selected by placing bits 5 to 7 at the appropriate states. For example, they are set at 101 to produce the pulsed output mode referred to earlier. This system of using a register to control the way in which a device functions is an important one to understand as it is a feature of so many computer peripherals.

The 6522 has all its registers at separate addresses, but this is not a feature of all computer interface devices. For example, the 6845 CRT controller (as used in the BBC machines) has some eighteen registers, but only occupies two addresses. The way in which this system operates is to have one address used to select the desired register, and the selected register then appears at the second address. For example, with the 6845, if you wish to access register 16 (the horizontal light pen register), 16 is written to the first address, and then the horizontal light pen value is read from the second address.

This system has the advantage of using up few addresses for input/output purposes, but has the disadvantage of requiring more instructions, especially if it is necessary to continuously access different registers. Some peripheral devices, such as the 6520 PIA, use a system where there are (say) six register, but only four addresses are used. This is very similar to the system just described, but there are perhaps just two registers sharing an address, with one bit of a control register being used to determine which of these can be accessed.

When using a high level language such as BASIC the programmer is largely isolated from the hardware of the computer by some sophisticated software. When using machine code this software is absent, and the programmer has to deal directly with the devices in the machine. With most practical machine code applications it is therefore necessary to have a good understanding of the computer you are using and its hardware, and you should try to find as much information of this type as possible.

INSTRUCTION SET CHART

Hexadecimal	Decimal	Instruction	Address Mode	Clock Cycles
00	0	BRK		7
01	1	ORA	Indirect X	6
05	5	ORA	Zero Page	4
06	6	ASL	Zero Page	6
08	8	PHP		3
09	9	ORA	Immediate	2
0A	10	ASL	Accumulator	2
0D	13	ORA	Absolute	4
0E	14	ASL	Absolute	6
10	16	BPL		2
11	17	ORA	Indirect Y	5/6
15	21	ORA	Zero Page X	4
16	22	ASL	Zero Page X	6
18	24	CLC		2
19	25	ORA	Absolute Y	4/5
1D	29	ORA	Absolute X	4/5
1E	30	ASL	Absolute X	7
20	32	JSR		6
21	33	AND	Indirect X	6

INSTRUCTION SET CHART (continued)

Hexadecimal	Decimal	Instruction	Address Mode	Clock Cycles
24	36	BIT	Zero Page	3
25	37	AND	Zero Page	3
26	38	ROL	Zero Page	5
28	40	PLP		4
29	41	AND	Immediate	2
2A	42	ROL	Accumulator	2
2C	44	BIT	Absolute	4
2D	45	AND	Absolute	4
2E	46	ROL	Absolute	6
30	48	BMI		2
31	49	AND	Indirect Y	5/6
35	53	AND	Zero Page X	4
36	54	ROL	Zero Page X	6
38	56	SEC		2
39	57	AND	Absolute Y	4/5
3D	61	AND	Absolute X	4/5
3E	62	ROL	Absolute X	7
40	64	RTI		6
41	65	EOR	Indirect X	6

INSTRUCTION SET CHART (continued)

Hexadecimal	Decimal	Instruction	Address Mode	Clock Cycles
45	69	EOR	Zero Page	3
46	70	LSR	Zero Page	5
48	72	PHA		3
49	73	EOR	Immediate	2
4A	74	LSR	Accumulator	2
4C	76	JMP	Absolute	3
4D	77	EOR	Absolute	4
4E	78	LSR	Absolute	6
50	80	BVC		2
51	81	EOR	Indirect Y	5/6
55	85	EOR	Zero Page X	4
56	86	LSR	Zero Page X	6
58	88	CLI		2
59	89	EOR	Absolute Y	4/5
5D	93	EOR	Absolute Y	4/5
5E	94	LSR	Absolute X	7
60	96	RTS		6
61	97	ADC	Indirect X	6
65	101	ADC	Zero Page	3

INSTRUCTION SET CHART (continued)

Hexadecimal	Decimal	Instruction	Address Mode	Clock Cycles
66	102	ROR	Zero Page	5
68	104	PLA		4
69	105	ADC	Immediate	2
6A	106	ROR	Accumulator	2
6C	108	JMP	Indirect	5
6D	109	ADC	Absolute	4
6E	110	ROR	Absolute	6
70	112	BVS		2
71	113	ADC	Indirect Y	5/6
75	117	ADC	Zero Page X	4
76	118	ROR	Zero Page X	6
78	120	SEI		2
79	121	ADC	Absolute Y	4/5
7D	125	ADC	Absolute X	4/5
7E	126	ROR	Absolute X	7
81	129	STA	Indirect X	6
84	132	STY	Zero Page	3
85	133	STA	Zero Page	3
86	134	STX	Zero Page	3

INSTRUCTION SET CHART (continued)

Hexadecimal	Decimal	Instruction	Address Mode	Clock Cycles
88	136	DEY		2
8A	138	TXA		2
8C	140	STY	Absolute	4
8D	141	STA	Absolute	4
8E	142	STX	Absolute	4
90	144	BCC		2
91	145	STA	Indirect Y	6
94	148	STY	Zero Page X	3
95	149	STA	Zero Page X	3
96	150	STX	Zero Page Y	3
98	152	TYA		2
99	153	STA	Absolute Y	5
9A	154	TXS		2
9D	157	STA	Absolute X	5
A0	160	LDY	Immediate	2
A1	161	LDA	Indirect X	6
A2	162	LDX	Immediate	2
A4	164	LDY	Zero Page	3
A5	165	LDA	Zero Page	3

INSTRUCTION SET CHART (continued)

Hexadecimal	Decimal	Instruction	Address Mode	Clock Cycles
A6	166	LDX	Zero Page	3
A8	168	TAY		2
A9	169	LDA	Immediate	2
AA	170	TAX		2
AC	172	LDY	Absolute	4
AD	173	LDA	Absolute	4
AE	174	LDX	Absolute	4
B0	176	BCS		2
B1	177	LDA	Indirect Y	5/6
B4	180	LDY	Zero Page X	3
B5	181	LDA	Zero Page X	3
B6	182	LDX	Zero Page Y	3
B8	184	CLV		2
B9	185	LDA	Absolute Y	4/5
BA	186	TSX		2
BC	188	LDY	Absolute X	4/5
BD	189	LDA	Absolute X	4/5
BE	190	LDX	Absolute Y	4/5
C0	192	CPY	Immediate	2
C1	193	CMP	Indirect X	6

INSTRUCTION SET CHART (continued)

Hexadecimal	Decimal	Instruction	Address Mode	Clock Cycles
C4	196	CPY	Zero Page	3
C5	197	CMP	Zero Page	3
C6	198	DEC	Zero Page	5
C8	200	INY		2
C9	201	CMP	Immediate	2
CA	202	DEX		2
CC	204	CPY	Absolute	4
CD	205	CMP	Absolute	4
CE	206	DEC	Absolute	6
D0	208	BNE		2
D1	209	CMP	Indirect Y	5/6
D5	213	CMP	Zero Page X	3
D6	214	DEC	Zero Page X	5
D8	216	CLD		2
D9	217	CMP	Absolute Y	4/5
DD	221	CMP	Absolute X	4/5
DE	222	DEC	Absolute X	7
E0	224	CPX	Immediate	2
E1	225	SBC	Indirect X	6

INSTRUCTION SET CHART (continued)

Hexadecimal	Decimal	Instruction	Address Mode	Clock Cycles
E4	228	CPX	Zero Page	3
E5	229	SBC	Zero Page	3
E6	230	INC	Zero Page	5
E8	232	INX		2
E9	233	SBC	Immediate	2
EA	234	NOP		2
EC	236	CPX	Absolute	4
ED	237	SBC	Absolute	4
EE	238	INC	Absolute	6
F0	240	BEQ		2
F1	241	SBC	Indirect Y	5/6
F5	245	SBC	Zero Page X	4
F6	246	INC	Zero Page X	6
F8	248	SED		2
F9	249	SBC	Absolute Y	4/5
FD	253	SBC	Absolute X	4/5
FE	254	INC	Absolute X	7

Note that only the codes that are used are shown in this table. In some addressing modes (Absolute X for example) the instruction may take additional clock cycle if crossing a page boundary.